Practice
Book
B

Macmillan
McGraw-Hill

B

The McGraw·Hill Companies

 Macmillan
McGraw-Hill

Published by Macmillan/McGraw-Hill, of McGraw-Hill Education, a division of The McGraw-Hill Companies, Inc.,
Two Penn Plaza, New York, New York 10121.

Printed in the United States of America

    6 7 8 9 10 045 09 08

Contents

Unit 2 • Growth and Change

Unit 3 • Better Together

Unit 4 • Land, Sea, Sky

© Macmillan/McGraw-Hill

Unit 5 • Discoveries

Unit 6 • Expressions

Name _____

A. Find at least five words in the puzzle that have the sound of short *a* or *i*. Start at any letter. Move from space to space in any direction to spell a word. The first one is done for you.

C	D	K	D	Y
L	S	N	R	N
P	I	T	A	S
M	T	H	A	T

B. Use five of the words you found to write sentences on the lines below.

1. _____

_____

2. _____

3. _____

4. _____

5. _____

At Home: Have your child name five other words that have the sounds for short *a* or *i* and use them in sentences.

Name _____

Find a word from the box to match each clue.
Write it in the puzzle.

carefully different excited groan tomorrow whisper

Across

2. the day after today

5. not the same

6. made very happy about something

Down

1. to make a sad sound

3. cautiously

4. to speak in a very quiet voice

As you read *David's New Friends,* fill in the
Character and Setting Chart.

Character	Setting

How does the information you wrote in this Character
and Setting Chart help you analyze story structure in
David's New Friends?

At Home: Have your child use the chart to retell the story.

David's New Friends • **Book 2.1/Unit 1**   3

Write a story. Create one or two interesting characters. Choose one of the settings from the box to use in your story.

- early Monday morning at home
- recess at school
- lunchtime in the school cafeteria
- after school in the science lab

_____

_____

_____

_____

_____

_____

_____

At Home: Have your child describe the characters and setting of other stories he or she has enjoyed. Encourage him or her to discuss the traits of the characters.

© Macmillan/McGraw-Hill

Name _____

As I read, I will pay attention to punctuation in each sentence.

	"You're doing very well, class," said Ms. Tallant.
8	The second graders were working on a mural. It was
18	a picture of their town, Greenville.
24	Each group was painting a panel. Each panel was
33	put up on the wall as it was finished. Their town was
45	all around their classroom!
49	Chenoa was working hard to finish her part of the
59	panel. She carefully painted the park, her favorite part
68	of town. She put herself in the picture with her dog, Bly.
80	The bell rang. Everyone except Chenoa packed up
88	for recess.
90	"It's recess, Chenoa," said Ms. Tallant. "You need
98	to get some fresh air." 103

Comprehension Check

1. What activity is the class doing in this scene? **Character and Setting**

2. What can you tell about Chenoa in this scene? **Character and Setting**

	Words Read	−	Number of Errors	=	Words Correct Score
First Read		−		=	
Second Read		−		=	

At Home: Help your child read the passage, paying attention to the goal at the top of the page.

Name _____

Look at the words in the box. Look at the guide words on each page. Write the words on the correct pages of the dictionary.

| friend | that | genuine | special | fun | sincere |

1.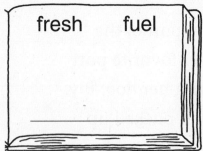
fresh   fuel

_____

2.
simple   speak

_____

3.
fruit   general

_____

4.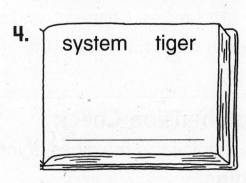
system   tiger

_____

5.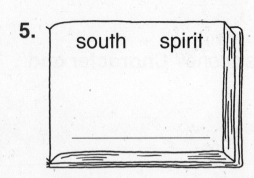
south   spirit

_____

6.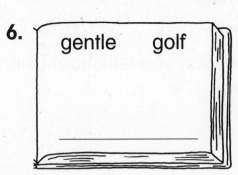
gentle   golf

_____

© Macmillan/McGraw-Hill

 At Home: Say a word and have your child look it up as quickly as he or she can in a children's dictionary. Ask him or her to tell you the guide words of the page where the word was found.

Name _____

A. Write the word for each clue.

1. opposite of *sit* _____

2. a baby sleeps in this _____

3. what you use to find your way _____

4. to excite _____

B. Circle the word that correctly shows the plural of each word in the box. Write the word on the line.

| baby | friend | penny | teacher | animal | supply |

5. pennys   pennies   pennyes _____

6. friends   friendes   friendies _____

7. supplies   supplyes   supplys _____

8. babbies   babies   babys _____

9. animalies   animals   animal _____

10. teacheries   teacher   teachers _____

At Home: Have your child name other word families that have the short *a* and *i* sounds. Then have your child choose two of the spelling words and write a story using them.

David's New Friends • **Book 2.1/Unit 1**   **7**

Write a caption for each picture.

1.

_____

_____

2.

_____

_____

3.

$2 \times 5 = 10$

_____

_____

4.

_____

_____

© Macmillan/McGraw-Hill

 At Home: Have your child choose a picture from a magazine and write a caption for it.

Name _____

**Use a word from the box to answer each riddle.
Write it on the line. Cross it off the list.**

ten	sun	mop	log	bed	cub	box	hen

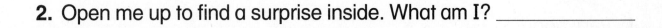

1. I shine up high in the sky. What am I? _____

2. Open me up to find a surprise inside. What am I? _____

3. I lay eggs. What am I? _____

4. Add one to nine to get me. What am I? _____

5. I am a baby bear. What am I? _____

6. Add water and use me to do a chore. What am I? _____

**Find the words in the box you did not use. Write a riddle
for each word.**

7. _____

8. _____

At Home: Point out a cup, a bed, and a box. Ask your child
to write the name of each at the top of a column and fill in
each column with words that share the same vowel sound.

Choose a vocabulary word from the box to match each clue. Write it on the line. One word will be used more than once.

thinning	company	wonderful
share	enjoyed	delighted

1. very good _____

2. people visiting your home _____

3. becoming less thick _____

4. very pleased and happy _____

5. companionship _____

6. had fun _____

7. to use or do with others _____

8. a business _____

**As you read *Mr. Putter & Tabby Pour the Tea*,
fill in the Story Map.**

Beginning

↓

Middle

↓

End

How does the information you wrote in this Story Map
help you analyze story structure in *Mr. Putty & Tabby
Pour the Tea*?

At Home: Have your child use the chart to retell the story.

Mr. Putter & Tabby Pour the Tea
Book 2.1/Unit 1

11

Name _____

Read the beginning part of the Story Map. Think about what could happen in the middle and at the end of the story. Fill in the story map with your ideas. Then use it to write your own story on the lines below.

> ### Beginning
> **Problem:** Shane can't find his favorite pen. He thinks his friend Mike took it.

Middle	End
How the character tries to solve the problem:	**How the problem is solved:**
_____	_____
_____	_____

_____

_____

_____

_____

_____

_____

_____

 At Home: Have your child describe the plots of his or her favorite stories by telling what happened in the beginning, middle, and end.

As I read, I will pay attention to punctuation and how it affects expression.

	"The creek is really dirty," said Marcella.
7	Mark frowned. "Look at how the reeds are thinning,"
16	he said. "I bet that's because the litter is getting in the
28	way of the plants. If this doesn't get cleaned up, all the
40	plants will die. The frogs won't have a home."
49	"Yes," said Marcella, "Someone should clean it up."
57	Mark nodded. "Maybe we should do it."
64	Marcella and Mark borrowed a garden rake, large
72	plastic bags and a box of plastic gloves from their mother.
83	Then they began to clear the litter from the creek.
93	They were so busy that at first they didn't notice they
104	were being watched. Marcella looked up.
110	"We have company," she said to Mark. 117

Comprehension Check

1. What do Marcella and Mark decide to do? **Plot**

2. What will happen to the frogs and plants if the creek is littered? **Draw Conclusions**

	Words Read	–	Number of Errors	=	Words Correct Score
First Read		–		=	
Second Read		–		=	

At Home: Help your child read the passage, paying attention to the goal at the top of the page.

Mr. Putter & Tabby Pour the Tea
Book 2.1/Unit 1 13

Name _____

Think about something you are doing with a friend today. Draw a picture of it in the box. Then write two sentences about it on the lines below. Use a verb that ends in _-ing_ in each sentence.

_____

_____

Think about something you did with a friend last week. Draw a picture of it in the box. Then write two sentences about it on the lines below. Use a verb that ends in _-ed_ in each sentence.

_____

_____

14 Mr. Putter & Tabby Pour the Tea
Book 2.1/Unit 1

Add *-ing* to the words below. Then use the new word in a sentence.

1. run _____

_____

2. sit _____

_____

3. set _____

_____

4. get _____

_____

5. stop _____

_____

6. hug _____

_____

© Macmillan/McGraw-Hill

🏠 **At Home:** Have your child write five more words that
end in *-ing*. Then ask him or her to write a sentence for
each new word.

Mr. Putter & Tabby Pour the Tea

◇ 15

Book 2.1/Unit 1

Name _____

You are helping write a list of rules for the new
playground. Look at the playground in the picture. Think
about what people should do to keep it safe and clean.
Then write six playground rules. Be ready to tell why
each one is important.

1. _____

2. _____

3. _____

4. _____

5. _____

6. _____

At Home: Ask your child to write a list of rules that everyone
in your home should follow. Invite your child to talk to you
about the reason for each rule.

Name _____

A. Choose a word from the box to answer each riddle below.

glad	lake	black	race	wag

1. I am all you see if you turn off the lights at night. I am the

   darkest color there is. What am I? _____

2. Dogs do this when they are happy. It is a way of moving.

   What is it? _____

3. If you want to swim, come on in. I am filled with water.

   What am I? _____

4. I am something you can win if you are quick. I am something

   horses, bikes, cars, and you can do. What am I? _____

B. Find the word in the box that you did not use. Write a riddle for it.

_____

_____

_____

At Home: Help your child write sentences with the words that he or she wrote on this page.

Fighting the Fire • **Book 2.1/Unit 1**   17

Name _____

A. Read the news article. Write words from the box to complete the sentence.

| heat | forest | flames | tell | safe |

Fire at Pepper Park

There was a fire yesterday in Pepper Park. It began when a

cookout fire spread into some trees in the _____.

Firefighter Ken Lee said, "The hot _____ hurt trees'

leaves and trunks. We are lucky that the fire got

only two trees. The rest are _____."

Firefighter Ken said that three people were at

a picnic near the fire. The _____ from

the fire burned their eyes. Firefighter Ken began to _____

people to leave. They got away fast, and they were all okay.

B. Write three sentences that tell how an unplanned fire could hurt things and people in a park near your home.

1. _____

2. _____

3. _____

Name _____

© Macmillan/McGraw-Hill

As you read Fighting the Fire, fill in the Main Idea and Details Web.

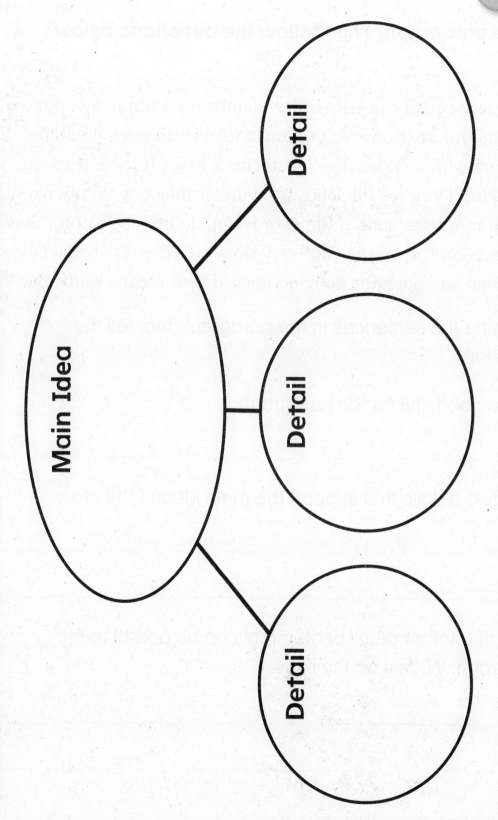

Main Idea

Detail

Detail

Detail

How does the information you wrote in this Main Idea and Details Web help you summarize Fighting the Fire?

At Home: Have your child use the chart to retell the story.

Fighting the Fire • **Book 2.1/Unit 1**   19

Read the paragraph. Then follow the directions below.

An escape plan can help every member of a family get out of a burning house. However, you must take extra steps if you are in a room with a closed door. First, check to see if there is smoke coming in. If you see smoke coming under the door, do not open it! Next, touch the door. If the door is hot, do not open it! If the door feels cool, open the door very slowly. If there is no smoke or heat when you open the door, go toward your escape route exit.

1. Underline the sentences in the paragraph that tell the main idea.

2. Write a good title for the paragraph.

_____

3. Write two details that support the main idea of the story.

_____

_____

4. Think of another detail or step that can be added to the paragraph. Write it on the lines.

_____

_____

_____

At Home: Read a news story or magazine article with your child. Have him or her underline the main idea of each paragraph. Ask your child to tell which details support it.

© Macmillan/McGraw-Hill

A. Look at the letters in the boxes. Use them to create words from the *-ell* and *-ame* families. Write your words on the line.

b	g	s
f	w	fl
sm	t	fr
c	sh	l
y	sp	n

_____

_____

_____

B. Write a poem about fire using your new words.

_____

_____

_____

_____

_____

At Home: Have your child find all the words in the *-ell* and *-ame* families with the same beginning sound/letter combinations (fell/fame, sell/same, and so on).

Fighting the Fire • **Book 2.1/Unit 1** ⟨**21**⟩

Name _____

A. This book's title page and table of contents are missing some parts. Find the missing parts in the lettered items below. Write the letter of each item on the correct line to complete the title page and table of contents.

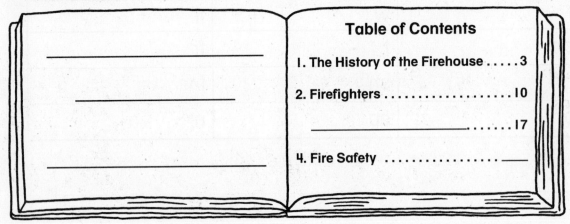

Table of Contents

1. The History of the Firehouse 3
2. Firefighters 10
_____ 17
4. Fire Safety . . . . ____

a. 3. *Who Uses the Firehouse*

b. *photographs by Ike Simmons*

c. 25

d. *by Jane Gray*

e. *Welcome to the Firehouse*

B. Read the possible index entries below. Circle the index entries that can be found in chapter four.

a. Firefighter's uniform 10–12

b. Having an escape plan 26–28

c. Firehouses in the 1800s 3, 4

d. Driving a fire truck 15, 16

e. Checking a door for heat 26

f. The siren 7, 15

g. Becoming a firefighter 16

h. Preventing fires 25, 31–36

© Macmillan/McGraw-Hill

 At Home: Invite your child to tell about a book he or she would like to write. What would be each chapter title?

As I read, I will pay attention to the punctuation and pronunciation of the vocabulary words.

	A wildfire is a burning **forest**. Wildfires can ruin land and
11	homes. They can hurt plants and animals. Sometimes they hurt
21	people, too.
23	Wildfires happen all around the world. They happen in forests
33	and grasslands. They usually happen in hot, dry, windy weather.
43	A wildfire starts like any other fire. It needs oxygen. Oxygen is
55	a gas in the air.
60	A fire also needs fuel. Fuel is something that burns. Wildfires
71	spread fast because trees, plants, and grasses burn quickly.
80	The most important thing a fire needs is **heat**. The heat might
92	come from lightning. It might come from sunlight shining
101	through glass. Or it might come from someone striking
110	a match. 112

Comprehension Check

1. What are three things that a wildfire needs to get started? **Main Idea and Details**

2. Do wildfires harm and destroy only plants and animals ? **Main Idea and Details**

	Words Read	–	Number of Errors	=	Words Correct Score
First Read		–		=	
Second Read		–		=	

At Home: Help your child read the passage, paying attention to the goal at the top of the page.

Fighting the Fire • Book 2.1/Unit 1   ◆ 23

Name _____

A. Add the suffixes *-er* and *-est* to the base words to create new words. Then write the new words in the correct column below.

base word	+ -er	+ -est
loud		
tough		
fast		
strong		
tall		

B. Write a story about the picture.
Use at least three of the new words you
created above and at least two words
that have long *a* and short *a* sounds.

_____

_____

_____

_____

_____

_____

At Home: Have your child write sentences that compare
things and people in your home using other words that end
in *-er* and *-est*.

A. Read the words in the box. Search for the words in the puzzle below. Circle each word as you find it. Then write the word in the correct column.

| ride | swim | white | skill | shin | time | wise | milk |

```
S   S   W   I   M   L   E   R
K   R   H   N   R   I   D   E
I   W   I   S   E   E   L   N
L   E   T   I   M   E   E   K
L   N   E   S   H   I   N   I
```

Words with the Short *i* Sound   **Words with the Long *i* Sound**

_____   _____

_____   _____

_____   _____

_____   _____

B. Write a sentence about what makes you special. Use at least two words that have the short *i* or long *i* sound.

_____

_____

At Home: Have your child make his or her own word search for short or long *i* words for you to solve.

Meet Rosina • **Book 2.1/Unit 1**   25

Name _____

Choose a word from the box to match each clue. Then use the word in a sentence.

language	relatives	signing	deaf	celebrate	cultures

I. cannot hear _____

_____

2. what you speak _____

_____

3. cousins, nephews, grandparents _____

_____

4. do this on holidays _____

_____

5. speaking with your hands and fingers _____

_____

6. customs and behaviors of groups of people _____

_____

As you read *Meet Rosina*, fill in the Main Idea and
Details Web.

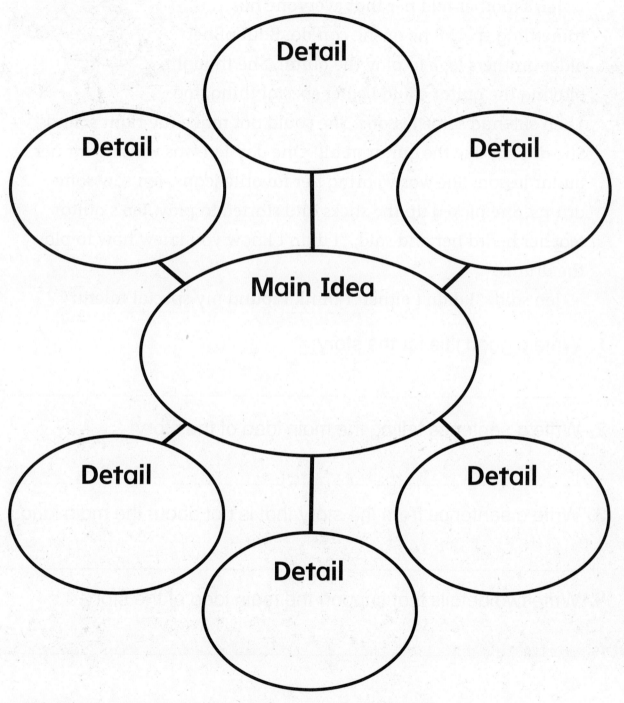

How does the information you wrote in this Main Idea and
Details Web help you summarize *Meet Rosina*?

At Home: Have your child use the chart to retell the story.

Meet Rosina • **Book 2.1/Unit 1** 27

Read the story. Then answer the questions.

Jen's mother told her that everyone has something special he or she can do. Both of her older brothers love to play the guitar. She thought playing the guitar could be her special thing, too. Then she had some lessons. She could not make the right sounds. She did not like the guitar at all! One day Jen was waiting for her guitar lesson. She was wearing her favorite jeans. Jen saw some drums. She picked up the sticks and started to play. Jen's guitar teacher heard her and said, "I didn't know you knew how to play the drums!"

Jen said, "I didn't either! I think I found my special talent!"

1. Write a good title for the story.

_____

2. Write a sentence telling the main idea of the story.

_____

3. Write a sentence from the story that is not about the main idea.

_____

4. Write two details that support the main idea of the story.

_____

_____

_____

At Home: Read a news story or magazine article with your child. Have him or her underline the main idea of each paragraph. Ask your child to tell which details support it.

Name _____

As I read, I will pay attention to the pronunciation of the vocabulary words.

10	People who cannot hear often "talk" to each other by **signing** with their hands. But many people do not understand
20	signing.
21	Today, **deaf** people who sign can talk to people who do not
33	understand signing. Dr. Jose Hernandez-Rebollar invented
40	a special glove. A computer in the glove translates **sign**
50	**language**. People hear the words through a computer's
58	speaker or read them on a screen.
65	Right now this special glove can only turn sign language
75	into English. In the future it will work in other **languages**, too.
87	This will help deaf and hearing people from many **cultures**
97	"talk" to each other. 101

Comprehension Check

1. How can deaf people who sign talk to people who do not understand sign language? **Main Idea and Details**

2. What will the rest of this piece be about? **Make and Confirm Predictions**

	Words Read	–	Number of Errors	=	Words Correct Score
First Read		–		=	
Second Read		–		=	

At Home: Help your child read the passage, paying attention to the goal at the top of the page.

Read the dictionary entry. Write an example sentence for each definition.

sign (sine) *noun* **1.** A symbol that means or stands for something. **2.** Something written, such as a poster, that gives information. *verb* **3.** To write your name. **4.** To use American Sign Language.

1. _____

_____

2. _____

_____

3. _____

_____

4. _____

_____

© Macmillan/McGraw-Hill

At Home: Have your child look through a dictionary to find another word with more than one meaning. Ask him or her to write a sentence for each meaning.

Name _____

A. Tim can follow only words that have the short *i* sound. Color Tim's path red.

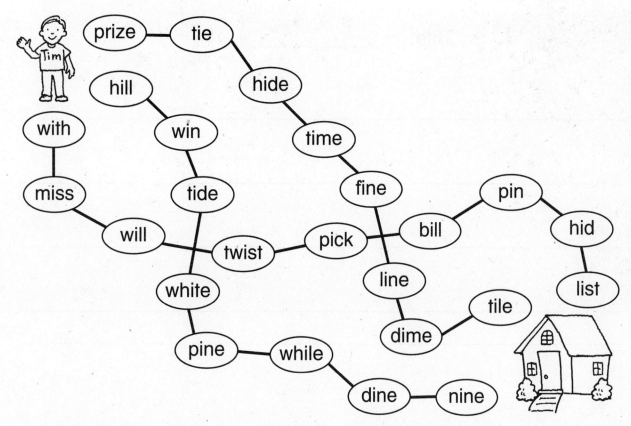

B. Circle the verbs with the long *i* sound. Then add *-ing* to each word you circled and write it on a line.

write	drip	drive	hid	chime
miss	lick	hide	trim	skip
ride	slip	mix	smile	twist

_____   _____   _____

_____   _____   _____

© Macmillan/McGraw-Hill

At Home: Have your child write sentences using six of the verbs from section B.

**Write a poem that tells about what makes you special.
Use words that rhyme. Then draw a picture to go with it.**

Title: _____

_____

_____

_____

_____

Name _____

Look at the puzzle. Find as many words as you can that have the long *o* and short *o* sound. Start at any letter. Move from space to space in any direction to spell a word. Write each word in the correct column below. The first two are done for you.

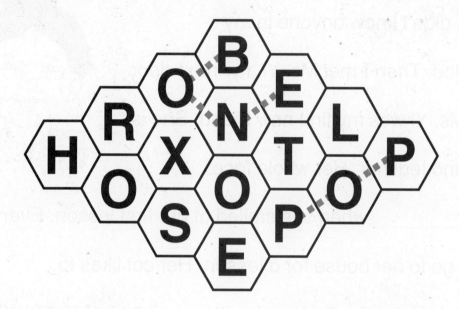

words with long *o*

bone

_____

_____

words with short *o*

pop

_____

_____

At Home: Ask your child to write a sentence for three of the words from each column.

Name _____

Read the story. Choose words from the box to complete the sentences.

| cuddle | favorite | patient | practiced | settled | wrinkled |

At first, I didn't know anyone in my

neighborhood. Then I met Ms. Yi, my next-door

neighbor. Ms. Yi was my first new friend. She is

also my piano teacher. Her whole face

_____ when she smiled at our first lesson. Every

Tuesday, I go to her house for a lesson. Her cat likes to

_____ on the bench with me while I play. Ms. Yi

waits for me to get _____ at the piano. Then she

asks, "Have you _____ ?" I always say yes,

because I try to practice every day. As long as she knows I'm

working hard, Ms. Yi is very _____ with me. She

never gets upset if I miss notes. The song I'm learning right now is

really hard. There are tons of notes! It's my _____,

so I'm going to play it until it's perfect.

Name _____

As you read *My Name Is Yoon*, fill in the Predictions Chart.

What I Predict	What Happens

How does the information you wrote in this Predictions Chart
help you summarize *My Name Is Yoon*?

At Home: Have your child use the chart to retell the story.

My Name Is Yoon • **Book 2.1/Unit 1** 35

Read the story. Then answer the questions below.

Jill watched the girls jumping rope. They had two ropes and were swinging them in great loops. A line of girls took turns jumping in and out of the swinging ropes. Suddenly, one of the girls turning the ropes noticed her. "Do you jump? Come on! Join us!" Jill hesitated.

Write a sentence that tells what might happen next.

_____

_____

Write a sentence that tells why you made your prediction.

_____

_____

Make up an ending to the story.

_____

_____

_____

At Home: Before reading a new story with your child, invite him or her to predict what the story will be about based on its title.

As I read, I will pay attention to the tempo and punctuation in each sentence.

	My name is Eva. These are some of the
9	entries in my diary. I wrote them when we lived
19	in Berlin, Germany.
22	April 1, 1933
23	Uncle Frank came over for dinner. He was
31	worried. He looked much older and his face
39	was so wrinkled. Nathan and I were sent to bed
49	early. We knew something was wrong, so we sat
58	at the top of the stairs and listened.
66	Uncle Frank told Mama and Papa that the
74	Nazis had come to his store. They painted black
83	across his doors. Then they posted signs that
91	said: "Don't buy from Jews." 96

Comprehension Check

1. Why do you think Uncle Frank looked older and worried? **Make and Confirm Predictions**

2. Are the Nazis friends of the Jews or against them? **Make and Confirm Predictions**

	Words Read	–	Number of Errors	=	Words Correct Score
First Read		–		=	
Second Read		–		=	

At Home: Help your child read the passage, paying attention to the goal at the top of the page.

A. Write each word +ed. Then write each word +ing. Watch for the two irregular verbs.

1. stop _____

2. jump _____

3. run _____

4. make _____

5. flip _____

B. Write a story about you and your friends using at least five of the new words you wrote.

_____

_____

_____

_____

_____

_____

_____

© Macmillan/McGraw-Hill

At Home: Write six to eight words in the past tense. Make a few "mistakes." Challenge your child to find and correct them.

◆ **Practice**

Short and Long *o*,
Inflectional Endings
-*s* and -*es*

Name _____

**A. Write a number or symbol under each letter below to
create your own code. Then write three short *o* words
and three long *o* words in your secret code.**

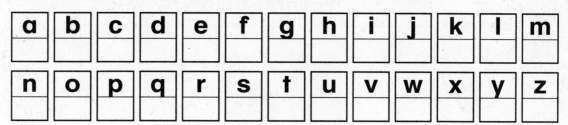

a	b	c	d	e	f	g	h	i	j	k	l	m

n	o	p	q	r	s	t	u	v	w	x	y	z

short ***o***   long ***o***

1. _____   4. _____

2. _____   5. _____

3. _____   6. _____

**B. Use the letters -*s* or -*es* to make the words below
mean more than one. Write the new word on the line.
Then use it in a sentence.**

1. bunny _____

_____

2. game _____

_____

3. friend _____

_____

4. penny _____

_____

At Home: Choose five more singular nouns. Ask your child
to make each noun plural by adding -*s* or -*es*.

Read the bar graph. Then circle the correct answer to each question.

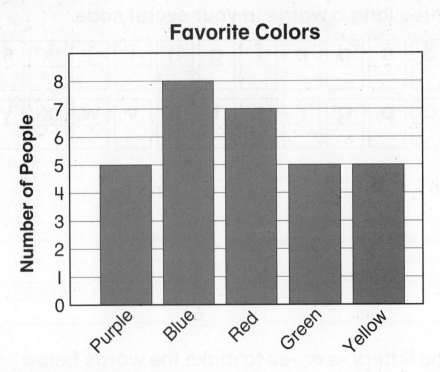

Favorite Colors

1. What is being compared?
   a. the color of the sky   **b.** the favorite color of each person asked

2. Which color was the most popular?
   a. red   **b.** yellow   **c.** blue   **d.** green   **e.** purple

3. Which colors got the same amount of votes as yellow?
   a. red and blue   **b.** green and purple

4. How many people like red?
   a. 10   **b.** 7   **c.** 4

5. What is the total number of people who voted?
   a. twenty   **b.** thirty-one   **c.** thirty

At Home: Have your child look through a newspaper and point out any bar graphs he or she finds.

Name _____

A. Find the words from the box in the puzzle below. Circle each word.

| mime | brake | shock | send | dunk |

```
r s h o c k g p w
d x v c g s b l m
y u z s r k d f i
h d n p i n l v m
b r a k e j c z e
m d x s b v g j p
```

B. Match each word to the word that means the *opposite* or almost the opposite. Write the letter of the answer on the line.

I. enjoyed ___   **a.** shout

2. safe ___   **b.** unhappy

3. carefully ___   **c.** hearing

4. delighted ___   **d.** disliked

5. whisper ___   **e.** dangerous

6. relatives ___   **f.** roughly

7. deaf ___   **g.** strangers

Use a word from the box to complete each sentence.

cultures	forest	tomorrow	favorite
company	flames	patient	practiced

1. The house caught fire and went up in _____.

2. Cuban Chinese food shows a mix of two different

   _____.

3. Judith likes strawberries best, but my _____
   is peaches.

4. Lea _____ at the piano each day so her playing
   would get better.

5. The family greeted their _____ at the front door.

6. Today is Friday, so _____ is Saturday.

7. Dad and I had fun hiking in the cool, green _____.

8. When you want to do something, it is hard to be

   _____ and wait your turn.

Name _____

A. Search for the words from the box. Circle each word you find.

| flute | sunny | mule | cube | luck | under |

```
M  J  S  U  N  N  Y  L  K  C
O  F  M  N  C  B  T  U  L  M
N  L  Y  D  Y  E  N  C  E  R
B  U  N  E  N  K  N  K  H  D
U  T  D  R  R  C  U  B  E  L
F  E  R  N  S  U  M  U  L  E
```

B. Write each word you found in the correct column below.

words with short u   words with long *u*

1. _____   4. _____

2. _____   5. _____

3. _____   6. _____

C. Write a sentence using two words from the box.

_____

_____

At Home: Help your child write a story using words with short *u* and long *u*.

© Macmillan/McGraw-Hill

The Tiny Seed • Book 2.1/Unit 2   43

Name _____

A. Write a sentence about plants for each word below.

1. burst _____

2. gently _____

3. drifts _____

4. drowns _____

5. neighbor _____

6. desert _____

B. Write two words from your sentences above that are verbs.

7. _____   8. _____

C. Write two words from your sentences above that are nouns.

9. _____   10. _____

As you read *The Tiny Seed*, fill in the Conclusion Chart.

Facts	**Facts**

Conclusion

How does the information you wrote in this Conclusion Chart help you summarize *The Tiny Seed*?

At Home: Have your child use the chart to retell the story.

Read each passage. Draw conclusions based on what you read.

1. In the spring Mary enjoyed the sunshine after several rainy days. Mary put on her gardening gloves and grabbed a shovel. She went outside and sat by the soil in her backyard. She held a small paper packet in her hand.

What is Mary going to do? _____

_____

_____

2. Chuck couldn't wait to get something special for his mother. He searched for the perfect gift. His mom liked gardening, and she enjoyed colorful displays. Chuck bought a container made of clay. It was filled with soil. There was something sticking out of the soil.

What did Chuck buy? _____

_____

_____

© Macmillan/McGraw-Hill

At Home: Have your child read part of a storybook. Have him or her draw a conclusion. Then continue reading to see if he or she came to the correct conclusion.

As I read, I will pay attention to the punctuation in each sentence.

	Some plants are packed with power!
6	Fresh fruits and vegetables are filled with vitamins and
15	minerals. They can keep you healthy. They can help you grow
26	and make you strong. They can give you energy. Plus, they are
38	fun to grow and taste great!
44	Some herbs and spices are also packed with power. These
54	plant bits add color and flavor to food.
62	Herbs can help you get better when you are sick. They can
74	even help you sleep well.
79	Fruits and vegetables are full of vitamins. Orange vegetables,
88	such as carrots, sweet potatoes, and pumpkins, have a lot of
99	Vitamin A. Do you like sweet fruits such as cantaloupe,
109	apricots, peaches, papayas, and mangoes? Their orange color
117	means they are packed full of Vitamin A, too. 126

Comprehension Check

1. What sorts of vegetables are rich in Vitamin A? **Draw Conclusions**

2. What is this selection about? **Plot**

	Words Read	–	Number of Errors	=	Words Correct Score
First Read		–		=	
Second Read		–		=	

At Home: Help your child read the passage, paying attention to the goal at the top of the page.

A. Use context clues to solve each plant riddle.

1. I stay green all year.
   Pinecones grow on me.
   What am I?

   _____

2. I can live in the desert where there is very little water. My leaves and stem store water inside. What am I?

   _____

3. I can be red, pink, or yellow.
   I have thorns on my stem.
   What am I?

   _____

4. I am orange. I am called a root vegetable because I grow underground. Rabbits like to eat me. What am I?

   _____

5. I am green. Cows and other animals graze on me.
   What am I?

   _____

6. I am yellow. I grow on stalks. There is a husk you have to remove before you eat me. What am I?

   _____

B. Write your own plant riddle using clue words. Have a friend solve it.

_____

_____

_____

At Home: Give your child other difficult words. Have him or her find out their meanings and then make up his or her own riddles for the words.

© Macmillan/McGraw-Hill

Name _____

A. Read the four words in each item. Cross out the one word that does not have the same vowel sound.

1. but   cub   bug   cube   2. dune   rude   rug   rule

3. rut   fuse   use   tune   4. rule   hum   jug   nut

B. Fill in the chart.

	add -er	add -est
strong	_____	_____
tall	_____	_____
hot	_____	_____

C. Draw a picture of two or three plants. Then write a sentence comparing the plants you drew. Use words from the chart.

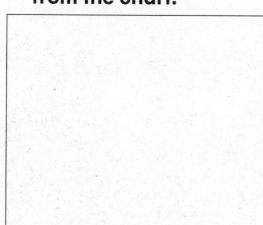

_____

_____

At Home: Have your child use some of the words from the
box above to write a paragraph.

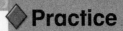
Make a diagram of your favorite tree or plant.
Label each part and tell what the part does for the plant.
Be sure to give your diagram a title.

Title: _____

At Home: Have your child find diagrams in encyclopedias or other reference sources.

Read each riddle. Fill in the missing letters to answer the riddle. Then draw a picture of what the answer names.

1. I am black and white and furry. I spray a stinky oil to protect myself.

_____unk

2. You can use me to eat. I am used for soup and ice cream.

_____oon

3. Birds live in me. They use twigs to make me. I can be found in a tree.

ne_____

4. On a hot day you can have me to cool off. I come in all kinds of flavors.

_____ ink

5. I am an instrument. You can play me with sticks

_____um

6. I am worn on the face. You can use me if you are in a show.

ma_____

At Home: Ask your child to tell you a word that rhymes with *lamp* and to name something you put on a letter before you mail it (*stamp*). Have your child write the word and circle the blend.

A Harbor Seal Pup Grows Up
Book 2.1/Unit 2

Name _____

Write two sentences to tell about each picture.
Use two words from the box in each sentence.

young   normal   rescued   examines   mammal   hunger

_____

_____

_____

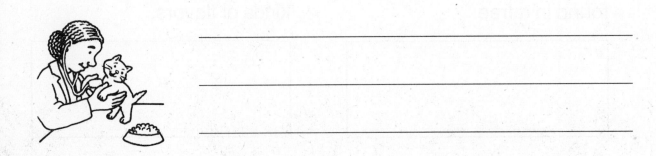

_____

_____

_____

_____

_____

_____

As you read *A Harbor Seal Pup Grows Up,* **fill in the Sequence Chart.**

Beginning

Middle

End

How does the information you wrote in this Sequence Chart help you summarize *A Harbor Seal Pup Grows Up?*

At Home: Have your child use the chart to retell the story.

A Harbor Seal Pup Grows Up
Book 2.1/Unit 2

53

Name _____

A. These story details got caught in a story scrambler. The order is all wrong! Unscramble the details and write them in a paragraph that shows the correct sequence.

Then she swam farther away by accident. Last she found her school! She heard the noise of the school bell and swam toward the noise. A fish named Juanita swam away from her school and got lost.

_____

_____

_____

_____

B. Add to the sequence above. Think of what could happen next. Then write a sentence about it on the lines below.

_____

_____

At Home: Have your child use the words *first, next, then,* and *last* to tell you what happened in the "Jack and Jill" rhyme.

© Macmillan/McGraw-Hill

Name _____

As I read, I will pay attention to the pronunciation of the vocabulary words.

9	Bald eagles were in danger of becoming extinct. Scientists **examined** the problem to find out the reasons why.
18	A bald eagle's habitat is near the sea. But people like to
30	live near the sea, too. Bald eagles can't always find places to
42	build their nests and lay eggs.
48	Bald eagles also have trouble finding food. They eat fish.
58	But people eat fish, too. Sometimes people catch too
67	many of the fish that bald eagles would eat. Then the birds
79	can die of **hunger**.
83	People and bald eagles don't want to eat the same food. Bald
95	eagles only like to eat fish that are sick and dying or already
108	dead. They actually leave the healthy fish for us. 117

Comprehension Check

1. Why is it difficult for bald eagles to find places to build their nests and lay eggs? **Sequence**

2. What are two reasons why bald eagles are threatened?
   Identify Main Idea and Details

	Words Read	–	Number of Errors	=	Words Correct Score
First Read		–		=	
Second Read		–		=	

At Home: Help your child read the passage, paying attention to the goal at the top of the page.

© Macmillan/McGraw-Hill

Write a second sentence to finish each sentence pair. In the second sentence, write an antonym for the underlined word in the first sentence. Circle the antonym you write.

Example: The <u>old</u> car was broken.

<u>The new car ran well.</u>

I. The elephant fell <u>down</u> a steep hill.

_____

2. The rescue team began a <u>long</u> trip to save the hurt elephant.

_____

3. The team drove <u>toward</u> the steep hill.

_____

4. They got out of their jeeps when they were <u>close</u> to the hill.

_____

5. They found the elephant at the <u>bottom</u> of the hill.

_____

© Macmillan/McGraw-Hill

At Home: Say the "Humpty Dumpty" rhyme. Ask your child to give you antonyms for at least two words in the rhyme.

Find and circle the words from the box in the puzzle below. Each word can be combined with another to form a compound word. Write the compound words on the lines below. Then circle the consonant blends in each word.

fish	drum	blue	tree	star
ear	break	plane	sky	space
scraper	top	suit	air	fast	bird

```
t s t a r x p g l f c d s
r k c m w g r b g i a v u
e y w b h q d i z s x s i
e b v l r m n r f h t j t
d i y u q e j d u z f p l
r r k e s p a c e m b l r
v d d f g l q k t b z a c
a l x e a r z v l t v n r
i b z j h b t o p f v e p
r u s c r a p e r l t x e
```

1. _____ 2. _____

3. _____ 4. _____

5. _____ 6. _____

7. _____ 8. _____

 At Home: Write these words: *ant, bow, mail, rain, box,* and *hill.* Ask your child to figure out a way to combine the smaller words to come up with three compound words.

© Macmillan/McGraw-Hill

Similes compare one thing to another. They use the words *like* or *as*.

Read each sentence. Then choose a simile from the box to tell what is happening. Write it on the line.

as dark as night	shine like stars
as cold as ice	as busy as a bee
sings like a bird	as strong as an ox

1. Maria worked quickly to get ready to go.

   Maria was _____.

2. A big storm moved in during the morning hours.

   The sky was _____.

3. Maria lifted heavy things to put them in the truck.

   You could see she was _____.

4. Maria's friend heard her sing as she loaded the truck.

   Her friend said, "Maria _____."

5. Maria picked up the snow with no gloves on.

   Her hands were _____.

6. Maria was so happy when she saw the dog's bright eyes.

   She told her friends, "His eyes _____."

At Home: Have your child tell you about someone he or she knows who *sings like a bird*. Ask your child about a time when he or she has seen something that *shines like a star*.

A. Write as many words as you can with long *a* spelled *ai* or *ay* to help explain the picture.

_____   _____   _____

_____   _____   _____

B. Underline all the words that have the sound of long *a* spelled *ai* or *ay*. Then draw a picture for each sentence.

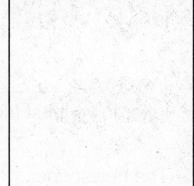

When they get back Rainy eats hay and a pail of grain.

Then Kay braids her horse Rainy's gray tail.

Kay rides Rainy down the driveway to get the mail.

© Macmillan/McGraw-Hill

At Home: Have your child write and illustrate sentences using some of the following words: *chain, brain, mail, nail, plain, day, bay, stay, may,* and *ray.*

A Trip to the Emergency Room
Book 2.1/Unit 2

59

Name _____

Choose a word from the box to complete each clue.
Write the word on the line. Then use the clues to
complete the puzzle.

serious	broken	personal	informs	heal

Across

3. This cast will help my arm to _____.

4. I'm glad I only have a cold and not a more _____
   illness.

Down

1. The jar fell and now it
   is _____.

2. I wrote a _____
   letter to my best friend.

5. The newspaper _____
   readers about what has happened.

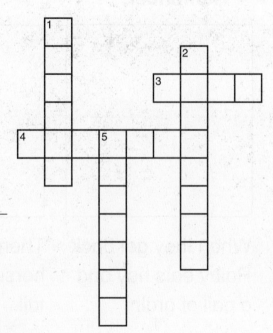

As you read *A Trip to the Emergency Room*, fill in the Sequence Chart.

First

↓

Next

↓

Then

↓

Last

How does the information you wrote in this Sequence Chart help you summarize *A Trip to the Emergency Room*?

At Home: Have your child use the chart to retell the story.

A Trip to the Emergency Room
Book 2.1/Unit 2

61

Name _____

Number the pictures to show the order in which things happen in the story. Write a sentence about each picture.

Jane Meets a Cat

_____

_____

_____

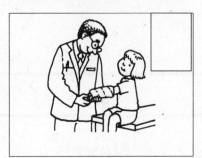

_____

_____

_____

_____

_____

_____

_____

_____

_____

_____

_____

_____

_____

_____

_____

© Macmillan/McGraw-Hill

62 A Trip to the Emergency Room
Book 2.1/Unit 2

Read each pair of homophones. Write the definitions.
Then write a sentence for each homophone.

1. hole: _____

_____

whole: _____

_____

2. right: _____

_____

write: _____

_____

_____

3. son: _____

_____

sun: _____

_____

© Macmillan/McGraw-Hill

At Home: Work with your child to think of several other pairs of homophones. Then ask your child to use each word in a sentence.

Choose a reference source from the box to answer each question.

> newspaper   almanac   telephone directory
> card catalog   globe   atlas

1. Where should you look for a book about diseases?

_____

2. Where could you find a chart of sunrise times for this year?

_____

3. Where could you find the address of a local doctor?

_____

4. Where could you find the final score of last night's ball game?

_____

5. Name two places to look if you want to find out where Antarctica is.

_____

6. Where would you look to see how much snow fell last year in your state?

_____

At Home: Have a "scavenger hunt" for information with your child. Use whatever resources are available at home.

As I read, I will pay attention to the pronunciation of the vocabulary words.

	Even if you are exercising and eating right, you
9	can still get sick. Germs can make you sick.
18	There are some simple things you can do to get
28	rid of germs. The easiest way is to wash your hands.
39	You should wash your hands after you use the
48	bathroom and before each meal.
53	Take care of your cuts. If the skin is **broken**,
63	germs can get into your blood. Ask an adult to help
74	you clean the cut. Use an antiseptic to kill any
84	germs. Then cover the cut with a bandage. These
93	steps will help the cut **heal**. 99

Comprehension Check

1. When should you wash your hands? **Sequence**

2. Should a cut heal if it is properly cleaned, disinfected, and bandaged? **Make and Confirm Predictions**

© Macmillan/McGraw-Hill

	Words Read	−	Number of Errors	=	Words Correct Score
First Read		−		=	
Second Read		−		=	

At Home: Help your child read the passage, paying attention to the goal at the top of the page.

A Trip to the Emergency Room
Book 2.1/Unit 2

65

Help Farmer Bay find his lost horse, Gray. Write the long *a* word that names each picture as you follow the maze.

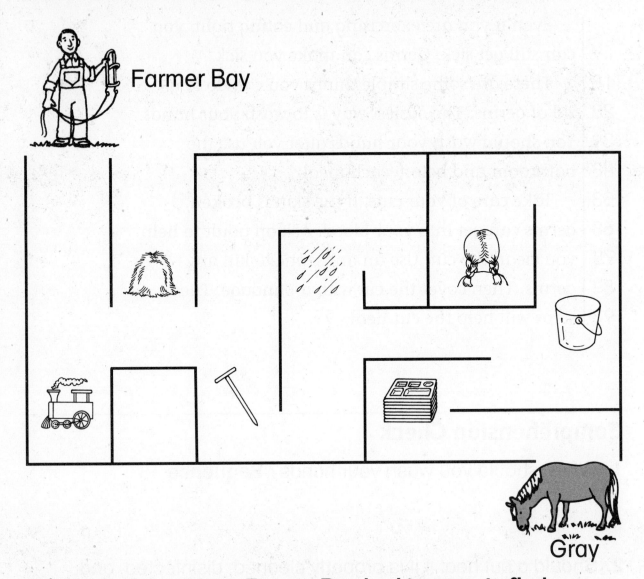

Farmer Bay

Gray

Name all of the things Farmer Bay had to pass to find his horse.

_____

_____

At Home: Have your child make up a poem using the words he or she wrote in the maze.

© Macmillan/McGraw-Hill

Name _____

A. Think of words that rhyme and are spelled with the same pattern as each word on the list. Write the words on the lines.

1. kind: _____

_____

2. pie: _____

_____

3. night: _____

_____

4. by: _____

_____

B. Write a rhyme using at least two of the words from the list.

_____

_____

_____

At Home: Have your child suggest other words that have the long *i* sound spelled *i, ie, igh,* and *y* that do not rhyme with the words listed above.

Name _____

A. Choose a word from the box to match each clue. Write it in the puzzle.

peered	giggled	snuggled
fluttered	vanished	recognized

Across

2. disappeared

5. flapped or waved rapidly

6. laughed in a silly way

Down

1. held close

3. known and remembered from past experience

4. looked with difficulty

B. Write two sentences about animals. Use at least one word from the box in each sentence.

7. _____

8. _____

As you read *Farfallina & Marcel,* fill in the
Inference Chart.

What I Learned From Reading	What I Already Know

My Inference

How does the information you wrote in this Inference Chart
help you to better understand *Farfallina and Marcel*?

At Home: Have your child use the chart to retell the story.

Farfallina & Marcel
Book 2.1/Unit 2 69

© Macmillan/McGraw-Hill

A. Read the following riddle. Make inferences to figure out the answer. Write it on the line.

I. Clue 1: I am Sam's best buddy.

Clue 2: I lick Sam's face to wake him up in the morning.

Clue 3: I bark and wag my tail when Sam comes home
from school.

Who am I?: _____

B. Write your own riddle about an animal. Follow the model above. Then write the answer at the bottom of the page.

2. Clue 1: _____

_____

Clue 2: _____

_____

Clue 3: _____

_____

Who am I? _____

At Home: Have your child read his or her clues for
you to guess the answer. Then take turns making
up riddles for objects or other animals.

© Macmillan/McGraw-Hill

As I read, I will pay attention to the punctuation and tempo in each sentence.

	Pip the emperor penguin started life as an egg.
9	His mother, Peggy, laid the egg just before she went
19	away. It was a beautiful white egg. She was very
29	proud of it.
32	All the females left together. They were
39	traveling across the ice to find food. They walked
48	toward the sea under a stormy sky.
55	"Isn't this fun?" they **giggled**.
60	Pip's father, Philip, watched as the females left.
68	He balanced Peggy's egg on his feet to keep it
78	warm. His feathers fluttered as the wind blew
86	across the Antarctic ice and snow.
92	All of the other fathers in the colony had an
102	egg to look after, too. They knew it was an
112	important job. 114

Comprehension Check

1. Why does Pip's father balance the egg on his feet above the ice? **Make Inferences**

2. Why does Peggy leave and travel across the frozen ice after she lays her egg? **Draw Conclusions**

	Words Read	–	Number of Errors	=	Words Correct Score
First Read		–		=	
Second Read		–		=	

At Home: Help your child read the passage, paying attention to the goal at the top of the page.

Farfallina & Marcel
Book 2.1/Unit 2

Name _____

Read the dictionary and thesaurus entries. Then follow the directions below.

Dictionary	Thesaurus
pitch(pich) *verb* to throw, hurl, or toss **place** (plās) **1.** *noun* where something is **2.** *verb* to put in a particular space	**pitch:** throw, fling, heave **place: 1.** *noun* area, spot, room, scene, setting **2.** *verb* set, arrange, position

1. Write a sentence that uses the word *pitch.*

_____

2. Write a sentence that uses a synonym of *pitch.*

_____

3. Write a sentence that uses the verb *place.*

_____

4. Write a sentence that uses a synonym for the verb *place.*

_____

5. Write a sentence that uses the noun *place.*

_____

At Home: Help your child use the other synonyms for *pitch* and *place* in sentences.

© Macmillan/McGraw-Hill

A. Use at least three words from the box to write a short story about a baby bird.

lie	fly	flight	sky	night	find	high	wild

1. _____

_____

_____

B. Write a contraction for each pair of words. Then use the contraction in a sentence. Write the sentence on the line.

2. we are _____

_____

3. it is _____

_____

4. could not _____

_____

At Home: Have your child use contractions to write his or her own sentences about zoo animals.

Name _____

A. Draw a picture in the box to go with each caption.

1.

This mother lion has
two cubs.

2.

The elephant calf follows
its mother.

**B. Think of two more baby animals. Draw a picture of each
one. Then write a caption for it on the lines below.**

3.

_____

_____

4.

_____

_____

At Home: Have your child find captioned photos and
pictures in magazines and newspapers, and make up
new captions to go with them.

© Macmillan/McGraw-Hill

Circle the words in each sentence that have the long *o* sound.

1. He puts the coat in the boat.

2. Joe is on the top team.

3. The soap makes lots of foam.

4. Are you a friend or foe?

5. My pet goat eats oats and can't stop eating them.

6. Let's go to the show before the others come.

7. My dad works in the garden with a hoe.

8. No, you can't row there in this fog.

9. I see a crow flying low over the barn roof.

Write two sentences about what you do to stay fit. Use at least two words that have the long *o* sound.

10. _____

_____

11. _____

_____

At Home: Say five long *o* words and have your child think of
a word that rhymes with each.

Name _____

Steven has written a letter to his friend Tia. Read the letter, then write the word from the box that tells what Steven is describing.

uniform	coach	starting	tryouts	practices	imaginary

Dear Tia,

I really want to be on the baseball team. Today I went to show

my baseball skills. _____ A man named Mr.

Long watched me play. His job is to help the baseball team get

better. _____ Everyone on the team wears

the same outfit. _____ The team meets every

Tuesday. At these meetings they work to improve their skills.

_____ If a player is really good, he or she can

play first in a game. _____ I think I did well

today. I hope I'm not just making that up in my mind!

_____

Your friend,

Steven

As you read *There's Nothing Like Baseball,* **fill in the Inference Chart.**

What I Know	What I Read

My Inferences

How does the information you wrote in this Inferences Chart help you to better understand *There's Nothing Like Baseball?*

 At Home: Have your child use the chart to retell the story.

There's Nothing Like Baseball
Book 2.1/Unit 2

77

© Macmillan/McGraw-Hill

Read the passage. Then answer the questions below.

Henry threw the ball to Sue. Sue caught it in her mitt and threw it back. Both Henry and Sue wore red uniforms. Henry's had a "34" on the back and Sue's had a "35."

"Do you think we're ready?" Sue yelled.

"Sure!" Henry shouted back across the field. They ran to join the other players wearing red uniforms. Players with blue uniforms were also beginning to arrive.

Sue and Henry saw their coach, Mr. Smith. Mr. Smith began waving all the starting players onto the field. A man with a whistle stood behind home plate.

1. Do you think Henry's and Sue's baseball team is getting ready for a game or for practice?

_____

_____

2. What clues did you use to find your answer?

_____

_____

_____

_____

At Home: As you read have your child tell what they know about different characters or situations based on visual or narrative clues.

© Macmillan/McGraw-Hill

**As I read, I will pay attention to punctuation
and expression.**

	"Come on, Amy," shouted Bindi. "Throw the football to me!"
10	Amy threw the football. It dropped quickly and tumbled
19	slowly along the ground.
23	She walked away and sat down on a bench. Amy didn't like
35	touch football **tryouts**. Everyone threw the ball too hard.
44	Plus, Amy had been sick and out of school for the last two
57	weeks. She still felt lazy.
62	Bindi ran over. "Come on, Amy," he said. "Try again! You
73	can do it."
76	Amy shook her head. "No. I only want to sit and watch now."
89	Coach Redmond saw that Amy was sitting on the bench.
99	"That's okay, Amy," he said. "You can rest. Bindi, let's keep
100	throwing, please." 112

Comprehension Check

1. Why does Amy sit down on the bench? **Make Inferences**

2. What does Amy do just before she goes to sit on the bench?
   Sequence

	Words Read	–	Number of Errors	=	Words Correct Score
First Read		–		=	
Second Read		–		=	

© Macmillan/McGraw-Hill

At Home: Help your child read the passage, paying
attention to the goal at the top of the page.

There's Nothing Like Baseball
Book 2.1/Unit 2

79

Name _____

Read the dictionary entry. Then write sentences for four of the definitions shown. Use the sentences in the definitions as models. Then write the number of the definition you used on the line next to each sentence.

press _verb_ 1. to use force on something; push. *Press the button to take a picture.* 2. to squeeze. *I will press juice from the lemon.* 3. to iron. *He will press the shirt to get the wrinkles out.* _noun_ 4. a tool or machine for pressing. *The press made small plastic pieces for toys.* 5. a machine for printing things. *The printing press uses paper on large rolls.* 6. the people who work for newspapers and magazines. *The press crowded around the movie star.*

1. _____

_____

2. _____

_____

3. _____

_____

4. _____

_____

At Home: Use a dictionary to find a word with more than one meaning. Challenge your child to write sentences for two or more meanings.

© Macmillan/McGraw-Hill

Read the story. Circle each long *o* word.

At first Joe was quiet, but then he spoke. "Can I tell you the tale of when my toe broke?"

I said, "Go ahead."

Joe said, "Well, I was standing outside in the snow. I heard a sound like the horn on a boat. I was scared," Joe said. "I ran as fast as I could go. Then I tripped on the ice and I broke my toe."

"What was the sound?" I wanted to know.

"Nothing scary," Joe said, "just a goat!"

In each sentence, circle the two words that can be made into a contraction. Write the contraction on the line.

1. We will have to be quick. _____

2. They have been here all day. _____

3. I have wanted to read that book. _____

4. She will love to pitch today. _____

5. We have won the game! _____

6. I will practice with my dad. _____

At Home: Write a silly story with your child using as many long *o* words as possible.

There's Nothing Like Baseball
Book 2.1/Unit 2
81

Name _____

Read the graph. Circle the correct answer to each question.

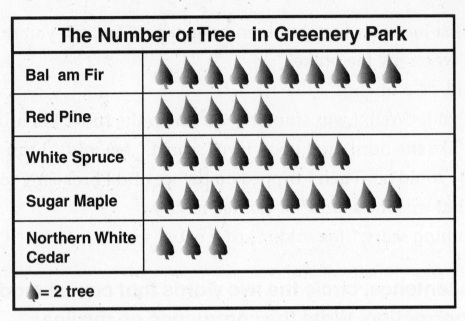

The Number of Tree   in Greenery Park

Bal am Fir	🌲🌲🌲🌲🌲🌲🌲🌲🌲🌲
Red Pine	🌲🌲🌲🌲🌲
White Spruce	🌲🌲🌲🌲🌲🌲🌲
Sugar Maple	🌲🌲🌲🌲🌲🌲🌲🌲🌲🌲
Northern White Cedar	🌲🌲🌲

🌲 = 2 tree

1. How many different types of trees are being compared?

   a. 3   **b.** 5   **c.** 10

2. How many balsam fir trees are there in Greenery Park?

   a. 4   **b.** 5   **c.** 20

3. Of which two types of trees are there the same amount?

   a. red pine and white spruce   **b.** sugar maple and balsam fir

4. How many more red pine trees than northern white cedar trees are there?

   a. 5   **b.** 1   **c.** 30

5. Ranger Barns planted more red pine trees. Now there are twice as many. How many red pine trees did she plant?

   a. 5   **b.** 10   **c.** 15

At Home: Help your child interpret the keys to any pictographs you see in newspapers or magazines .

Name _____

A. In the space below, make a sign to announce tryouts for a sports team. Use these words in your sign.

> tryouts   coach   practices   Friday   right   serious

1.

[blank box]

B. The sentences below are FALSE. Rewrite each sentence so that it is true. Use the word in dark type in your sentence.

2. Something that **drifts** moves very fast.

_____

3. A **mammal** is an animal with feathers.

_____

4. The vase was **broken** because it was all in one piece.

_____

5. The storm cut off the power so we ate by the **glow** of an

electric lamp. _____

A. Make up a title for each book cover. Use the words in the box.

vanished	neighbor	recognized	peered

1.

_____

_____

2.

_____

_____

3.

_____

_____

4.

_____

_____

B. Complete each sentence with a word from the box.

drowns	hunger	examines	sleeping

1. If you water a plant too much, it _____.

2. A detective _____ a crime scene.

3. The baby is _____ quietly in her crib.

4. Was it pain or _____ that made the baby cry?

© Macmillan/McGraw-Hill

Name _____

Read the sentence. Write the correct letters from the box to complete the words.

e	ea	ee	ey	y

1. I ate m_____t and ch_____se for lunch.

2. We saw a monk_____ at the zoo.

3. Nicole had a dr_____m that she was a tin_____,

   little lad_____.

4. Rory hung his painting on an _____sel.

5. Pl_____se cl_____n up to help k_____p our

   Earth b_____utiful.

🏠 **At Home:** Help your child write a poem using long *e* words.

Head, Body, Legs • **Book 2.1/Unit 3** ◆85◆

Read each sentence. Write _T_ if the sentence is true. Write _F_ if the sentence is false. In each sentence, underline the vocabulary word from the word box.

breathe   swung   gasped   delicious   frantically   attached

1. Foods that are delicious are tasty. ____

2. A person moves frantically if they are calm. ____

3. Your arm is attached to your foot. ____

4. It is not important to breathe. ____

5. A monkey may have swung on a branch. ____

6. Your leg is attached to your ankle. ____

7. Most people like to eat delicious food. ____

8. Gasped means to have breathed easily. ____

Name _____

**As you read *Head, Body, Legs: A Story from Liberia,* fill
in the Cause and Effect Chart.**

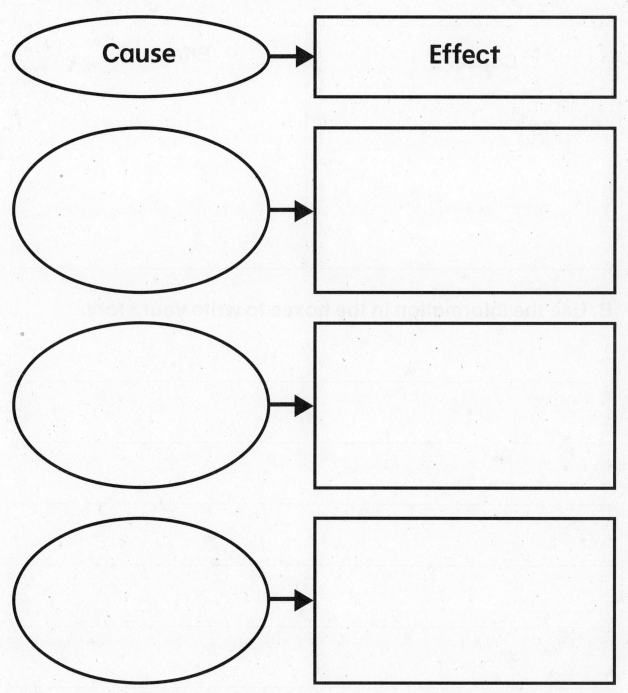

How does the information you wrote in this Cause and Effect Chart
help you to better understand *Head, Body, Legs: A Story from Liberia*?

At Home: Have your child use the chart to retell the story.

Head, Body, Legs • **Book 2.1/Unit 3** **87**

© Macmillan/McGraw-Hill

Name _____

**A. Think of a story plot about teamwork. Use the cause
and effect boxes below to plan your story.**

Cause	Effect

B. Use the information in the boxes to write your story.

_____

_____

_____

_____

_____

_____

At Home: Discuss the idea of cause and effect using things
that happen every day. For example: There was water on the
floor. I cleaned it up.

As I read, I will pay attention to the punctuation in each sentence.

	Once upon a time, there was a young man who had no
12	family and no job. He was poor and hungry.
21	One day he took a walk through the woods near his town.
33	He heard noises coming from some bushes.
40	He pushed aside the branches. There he found a little
50	dog that had become attached to some vines. The young
60	man helped set it free. Then he gave the dog a few stale
73	pieces of bread that he had in his pocket.
82	He was very surprised when the dog spoke to him.
92	"You have been kind to me," said the little dog. "In
103	return, I will tell you how to find treasure. Do you see that
116	big oak tree over there? Dig a hole at the base of
128	its trunk." 130

Comprehension Check

1. Why does the dog tell the man how to find treasure? **Cause and Effect**

2. How did the man happen to find the little dog trapped in the vines? **Draw Conclusions**

	Words Read	–	Number of Errors	=	Words Correct Score
First Read		–		=	
Second Read		–		=	

© Macmillan/McGraw-Hill

At Home: Help your child read the passage, paying attention to the goal at the top of the page.

Head, Body, Legs • Book 2.1/Unit 3

Read the story below. Use context clues to help you figure out the meaning of each word in dark print. Underline the context clues. Then write the definitions on the lines.

   Camp Colby went on a camping trip. Brian, Mark, and Shelly wanted to put up the tent. First they had to find a good **campsite**. They found a good place to put up the tent right away. The campsite was in a flat area next to a **water source**. They did not have to walk far to the stream for fresh water. Next Brian checked to see if they had all the **hardware** for the tent. Putting up the tent would be impossible without the right tools. The tent needed to be **secure** or steady so that it wouldn't fall down. After they finished putting up the tent, Mark and Brian searched for firewood. They were careful not to go outside the **perimeter** of the campsite. If Mark and Brian were to go outside of the campsite area, they could get lost.

1. campsite: _____

2. water source: _____

3. hardware: _____

4. secure: _____

5. perimeter: _____

At Home: Have your child read his or her story aloud. Invite him or her to point out the details in the picture that were used in his or her story.

© Macmillan/McGraw-Hill

Use each word from the box to write a sentence below. Then draw a picture for one of the sentences you wrote.

| cheerful | sleepless | beautiful | eventful |

1. _____

_____

2. _____

_____

3. _____

4. _____

_____

At Home: Have your child write a short story using three or four words with the suffixes *-ful* and *-less* .

Head, Body, Legs • **Book 2.1/Unit 3** 〈**91**〉

Make up your own home page. Then add the names of possible links in each drop-down menu. Draw pictures next to some links.

My name is _____.

My Family

_____

_____

_____

_____

My Favorite Things

_____

_____

_____

_____

My Hobbies

_____

_____

_____

Things I Like to Do

_____

_____

_____

© Macmillan/McGraw-Hill

At Home: Explore the Web with your child to look at different Web sites and the kinds of information they have.

Name _____

A. Add one letter to change each short *u* word into a long *u* word.

1. hug

   hug___

2. cub

   cub___

3. us

   us___

4. cut

   cut___

B. Show two ways to change *tub* into a long *u* word.

5. tub___

6. tub___

C. Add a consonant to each word to create a long *u* word.

7. fu___e

8. Ju___e

9. reu___e

10. u___ited

D. Think of two long *u* words. Write a sentence using each word.

11. _____

_____

12. _____

_____

At Home: Ask your child to tell you the name of a country that has a long *u* in its name. Example: Cuba

Officer Buckle and Gloria
Book 2.1/Unit 3

93

Name _____

Use the code to figure out the words. Then write them in a sentence.

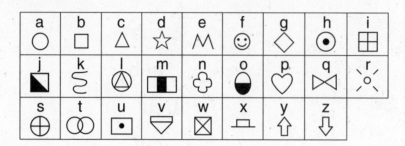

1. □ ⊡ ☆ ☆ ⇧ _____

_____

2. ○ ⊙⊙ ⊙⊙ M ♣ ⊙⊙ ⊞ ⬯ ♣ _____

_____

3. ⬯ □ M ⇧ ⊕ _____

_____

4. M ♣ ⬯ ✳ ▨ ⬯ ⊡ ⊕ _____

_____

5. ○ △ △ ⊞ ☆ M ♣ ⊙⊙ _____

_____

6. ⊙⊙ ⊞ ♡ ⊕ _____

_____

**As you read *Officer Buckle and Gloria,* fill in the
Illustrations Chart.**

Illustration	What I Learn From the Picture

How does the information you wrote in this Illustrations Chart help
you to better understand *Officer Buckle and Gloria*?

At Home: Have your child use the chart to retell the story.

Officer Buckle and Gloria
Book 2.1/Unit 3
95

© Macmillan/McGraw-Hill

Draw an illustration to go with each sentence. Your illustrations should help readers understand the sentence.

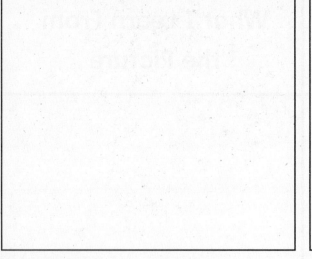

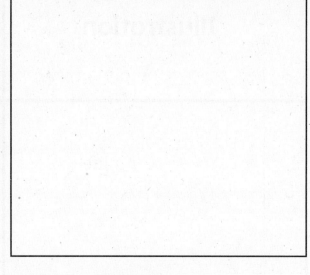

1. The girl wore her helmet when she skated.

2. The children get on the bus in a single-file line.

3. We couldn't swim at the pool because the lifeguard was not at the lifeguard stand.

4. We stay far away from the crocodiles at the zoo.

© Macmillan/McGraw-Hill

 At Home: Ask your child to draw four pictures that will help the reader understand steps in planting and caring for a flower.

As I read, I will pay attention to the punctuation in each sentence.

	Boat rides are a great way to be near the water without getting
13	wet. Follow these rules to stay safe while boating.
22	**Safe Boating Tips**
25	• Never go on a boat without an adult.
33	• Check the weather before you leave. Don't get in a boat if a
46	storm is coming.
49	• Always wear a life jacket.
54	• Be careful when you get in and out of a boat. It's easy to slip
69	and fall in the water.
74	• Don't jump around on a boat. The boat can tip over.
85	• Don't jump or dive from a boat before asking an adult. There
97	could be a rock or other sharp objects under the water.
108	People who have problems with their boats at sea can get help
120	from the U.S. Coast Guard. The Coast Guard watches over the
131	coastline and the seas. 135

Comprehension Check

1. What is the Coast Guard mainly responsible for? **Character and Setting**

2. Why is it a good idea to wear a life jacket on a boat ride? **Make Inferences**

	Words Read	–	Number of Errors	=	Words Correct Score
First Read		–		=	
Second Read		–		=	

© Macmillan/McGraw-Hill

At Home: Help your child read the passage, paying attention to the goal at the top of the page.

Officer Buckle and Gloria
Book 2.1/Unit 3
97

Name _____

A. Think of a synonym for each underlined word. Write a new sentence with the synonym. Circle the synonym after you write the new sentence.

1. A storm was about to <u>begin</u>.

_____

2. We were in the park, so we had to <u>go.</u>

_____

3. We ran <u>quickly</u>.

_____

4. <u>Big</u> clouds grew gray in the sky.

_____

_____

B. Think of two more words that are synonyms. Use each one to write a sentence.

5. _____

6. _____

At Home: With your child, sing "Twinkle, Twinkle, Little Star".
Ask your child to choose at least two words from the song
and tell you synonyms for each one.

© Macmillan/McGraw-Hill

Name _____

A. The mule is lost. Complete the maze to help Farmer June find her mule. Write the word that names each picture.

| June | mule | cube | tuba | flute | tube |

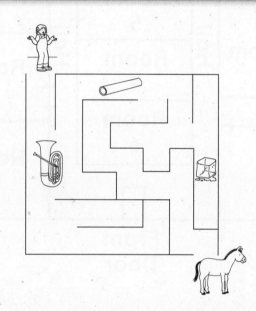

B. Use all the words in the box to write a silly story about how Farmer June found the mule.

_____

_____

_____

_____

_____

At Home: Have your child use the words *mule*, *Duke*, and *cute* in one sentence.

Read the floor plan. Answer the questions.

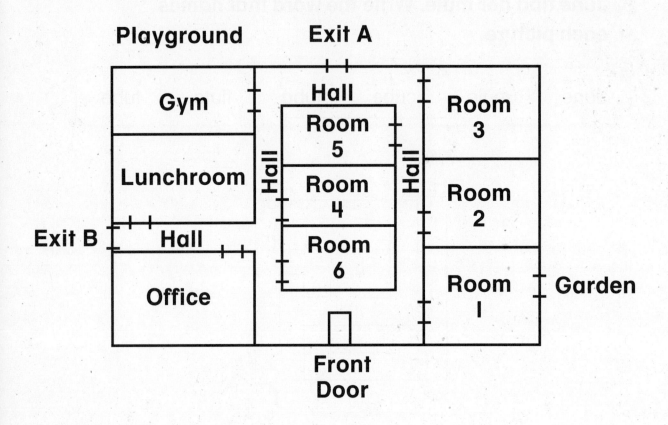

Playground   Exit A

Gym   Hall   Room 3
Room 5

Hall   Lunchroom   Room 4   Hall   Room 2

Exit B   Hall   Room 6

Office   Room 1   Garden

Front Door

1. Which 3 rooms are closest to exit A?

_____

2. Which room is closest to the garden? _____

3. Which two rooms are closest to exit B? _____

_____

4. There is a fire drill. Lola is in Room 6. She must take the fastest way out of the building. Which exit should she use?

_____

At Home: Have your child draw a floor plan of your home and label each room.

A. Create as many words as you can using the consonant digraphs and word parts below. Write the new words you make.

th		-in
sh	+	-eat
wh		-ip
ch		-opper
		-orn

_____ _____ _____

_____ _____ _____

_____ _____ _____

_____

B. Write two sentences using three or more of your new words.

1. _____

_____

2. _____

At Home: Have your child write tongue-twisters using the words he or she wrote on this page.

Meet the Super Croc
Book 2.1/Unit 3

101

Name _____

Write one sentence for each word below.

1. ancient _____

_____

2. confirm _____

_____

3. valid _____

_____

4. hopeful _____

_____

5. unable _____

_____

Draw a picture that shows what happens in one of your sentences.

Name _____

As you read *Meet the Super Croc,* **fill in the Summary Chart.**

> **Main Idea**

> **Main Idea**

> **Main Idea**

> **Summary**

How does the information you wrote in this Summarize Chart help
you to better understand *Meet the Super Croc*?

At Home: Have your child use the chart to retell the story.

Meet the Super Croc
Book 2.1/Unit 3

103

© Macmillan/McGraw-Hill

Name _____

Read the article. Write a good title for it. Then write two or three sentences that summarize the article.

_____

John James Audubon studied birds in the wild. He spent his life learning about birds and other animals. It was a life that made him famous.

John got interested in birds as a boy. He was born in 1785 in what is now Haiti. He went to school in France. He came to America at 18. He moved from state to state. He kept changing jobs. John liked birds more than anything else. He made many drawings of the birds he loved. In time John put out a book called *The Birds of America*. It took ten years to finish. The book is still read worldwide. Later in life he began a book about mammals. He died before that book was done.

Audubon was a great artist. He was also a great scientist. He gave the world valuable art and facts about wildlife.

_____

_____

_____

_____

 At Home: Have your child write a summary of his or her experiences in first grade in just two or three sentences.

Name _____

A. Use the prefixes, base words, and suffixes below to write a list of new words.

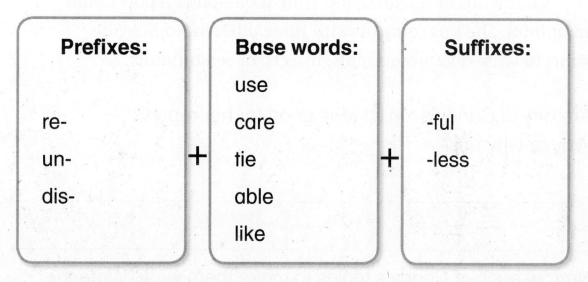

Prefixes:		Base words:		Suffixes:
re-	**+**	use care tie able like	**+**	-ful -less
un-				
dis-				

_____   _____   _____

_____   _____   _____

_____   _____   _____

_____   _____   _____

B. Write four sentences using as many of your new words as you can. Add -s, -ed, or -ing to the ends of words if you need to.

I. _____

2. _____

3. _____

4. _____

At Home: Challenge your child to add *both* a prefix *and* a suffix to the base word *use*.

Read the sentences below. Then answer the questions.

Candy has to research and write a one-page report about an animal. She has come up with three different topics. She wants to write about mammals, insects, or sea animals.

1. Are any of Candy's topic ideas good for her report? Why or why not?

_____

_____

2. Narrow each of Candy's topics to make them work. Write the three new topics on the lines.

a. mammals _____

b. insects _____

c. sea animals _____

3. Read the new topics you have written above. Write them on the lines in the first column below. Now narrow each new topic so that it is even more specific. Write your responses on the lines in the second column.

a. _____   _____

b. _____   _____

c. _____   _____

© Macmillan/McGraw-Hill

At Home: Have your child write three topic ideas that would work well for a one-page report. Have him or her explain why they made the choices he or she did.

As I read, I will pay attention to punctuation and the pronunciation of the vocabulary words.

	Most kinds of animals that lived a long time ago are no longer
13	living. Scientists think that 99.9 percent of all species that have
23	ever lived are now extinct. Some animals died because they were
34	**unable** to adapt to changes in the world. Others died in
45	earthquakes and floods.
48	But there are some species that have survived for millions of
59	years and have not changed much. Some people call them
69	"living fossils." Like real fossils, living fossils can help us learn
80	about the past.
83	One example of a living fossil is a coelacanth (SEE-luh-kanth).
92	This **ancient** fish still lives in the Indian Ocean. It looks the same
105	as real fossils of coelacanths that are 400 million years old.
115	Sharks have lived in the sea for more than 350 million years. 126

Comprehension Check

1. What are some of the reasons that animals from long ago no longer exist today? **Summarize**

2. What is an example of a "living fossil"? **Main Idea and Details**

	Words Read	–	Number of Errors	=	Words Correct Score
First Read		–		=	
Second Read		–		=	

At Home: Help your child read the passage, paying attention to the goal at the top of the page.

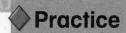
Write a short story about finding something that lived
on Earth millions of years ago. Use at least ten words
from the box. You can add the word endings *-ed, -ing, -s,*
or *-es* to some of the words if you need to.

rejoin	uncover	teeth	remove	unusual
shovel	discover	unlike	research	these
rebuild	when	reload	sharp	then
shape	shin	disconnect	unforgettable	where

_____

_____

_____

_____

_____

_____

_____

At Home: Challenge your child to think of as many words as
he or she can with the prefixes *re-, un-,* and *dis.* Have your
child explain how the prefix changes each word's meaning.

Name _____

A. Finish the words by adding *th, sh, ph, ch,* or *tch*.

1. ben _____

2. ca _____ er

3. fre _____

4. boo _____

5. lea _____

6. _____ one

7. ma _____ ematics

8. wa _____

B. Write a story that includes at least four words that you wrote above.

_____

_____

_____

_____

_____

_____

At Home: Help your child find words with *th, sh, ch,* and *tch* in a book or magazine. Ask him or her to use the words he or she found in a sentence.

The Alvin Ailey Kids
Book 2.1/Unit 3

109

Name _____

Write a letter to a friend about a special event at your school. The event can be real or made up. Use all of the words from the box.

| remember | students | perform | effort | proud | mood |

Dear _____,

_____

_____

_____

_____

_____

Your friend,

_____

The Alvin Ailey Kids
Book 2.1/Unit 3

© Macmillan/McGraw-Hill

Name _____

As you read *The Alvin Ailey Kids: Dancing As a Team,*
fill in the Summarize Chart.

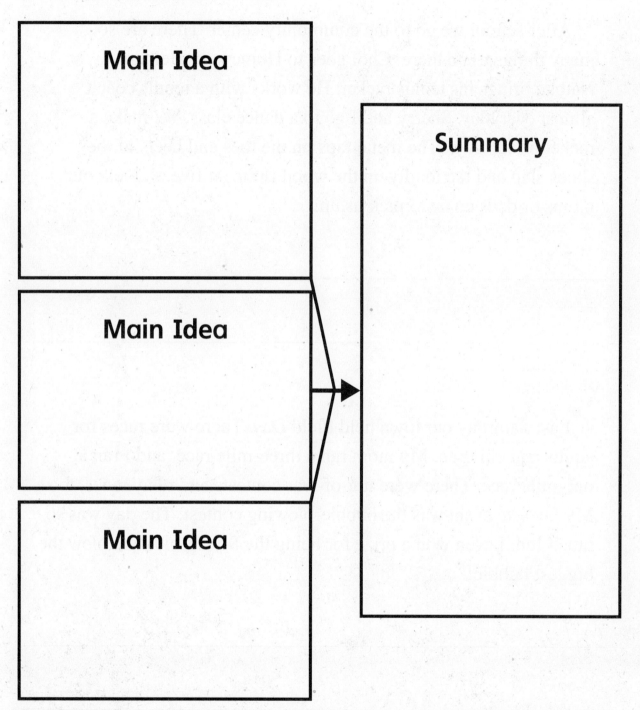

Main Idea

Main Idea

Main Idea

Summary

How does the information you wrote in this Summarize Chart help
you to better understand *The Alvin Ailey Kids: Dancing As a Team?*

At Home: Have your child use the chart to retell the story.

The Alvin Ailey Kids
Book 2.1/Unit 3

111

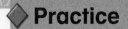
Read each story. Write a sentence to summarize each story.

After school we go to the community center. There are so many things to do there. Choi goes to Homework Helpers. Nathan brings his tennis racket. He works with a tennis coach almost everyday. Sherry and I go to a dance class. We make a racket of our own! The metal taps on the toes and heels of the shoes slap and tap loudly on the wood floor. At five o'clock, our moms or dads come to pick us up.

_____

_____

Last Saturday our town held Field Day. There were races for adults and children. My mom ran a three-mile race, and I ran a one-mile race. There were tug-of-war contests and relay races, too. My favorite event was the bubble-blowing contest. The day was so much fun. I even won a prize for being the 8-year-old who blew the biggest bubble!

_____

_____

 At Home: Have your child summarize his or her day at school or an afternoon activity in one or two sentences.

As I read I will pay attention to the punctuation.

"Everything I do comes from my being a dancer. I love tap,
12 | and I'll do it until I can't."

19 | Gregory Hines said that in 1997. At that time, he had been
30 | a dancer for 48 years! Gregory was born in New York City in
42 | 1946. His family lived on Sugar Hill, in Harlem. Gregory
51 | started tap dancing when he was just five years old.

61 | Gregory and his brother Maurice were good **students**. They
70 | started a tap dancing act when Gregory was only six years old.
82 | They called themselves the Hines Kids. They learned a lot by
93 | watching other good tap dancers. The Hines Kids became
102 | good too!

104 | During the week, Gregory and Maurice would go to school.
114 | But every weekend, they would **perform**. They performed
122 | even when Gregory hurt his right eye in an accident. 132

Comprehension Check

1. What was life like for the Hines Kids? **Summarize**

2. How do you know Gregory was dedicated to performing?
Summarize

	Words Read	–	Number of Errors	=	Words Correct Score
First Read		–		=	
Second Read		–		=	

 At Home: Help your child read the passage, paying
attention to the goal at the top of the page.

The Alvin Ailey Kids
Book 2.1/Unit 3

113

Use the dictionary and thesaurus entries to answer the questions.

Dictionary	Thesaurus	
actor (**ak**-tur) *noun* A person who performs a part.	**actor**	*synonym:* entertainer, performer
		antonym audience, spectator, fan
persevere (**per**-suh-veer) *verb* To continue to try in spite of difficulties.	**persevere**	*synonym:* continue, endure, persist
		antonym quit, surrender

1. Which word is a noun? _____

2. What is the pronunciation of *persevere*? _____

3. *Quit* and *surrender* are antonyms of which word?

_____

4. What is the definition for *actor*? _____

_____

5. What is an antonym for *actor*? _____

© Macmillan/McGraw-Hill

At Home: Have your child read a review of a performance in the newspaper. Help him or her list interesting words from the review. Then have your child find antonyms for each word.

Read each word. Write *closed syllable* if the word ends with a closed syllable. Write *open syllable* if the word ends with an open syllable. Then add the letters *ch*, *sh*, *th*, or *tch* to the beginning or end of each word to make a new word. Write the new word on the line.

1. pit _____

2. elf _____

3. tea _____

4. no _____

5. arm _____

6. be _____

7. out _____

8. hi _____

9. boo _____

10. row _____

At Home: Have your child find examples of words with open
and closed syllables in a book he or she is reading.

Alliteration is the repeated use of the same beginning
sound in a group of words.

Rhythmic patterns are sounds and words that repeat to
make a rhythm.

Read the lyrics to this folk song. Then follow the directions.

It was on a bright September morn as all in bed we lay,
Our mother called to say to us, "Today is cleaning day."
For it's sweep, sweep, wipe, wipe, wash, wash away.
We're all at work about the house upon a cleaning day.

It was on a bright September morn as all in bed we lay,
Our father called to say to us, "Today is painting day."
For it's stir, stir, dip, dip, brush, brush away.
We're all at work about the house upon a painting day.

1. Draw a circle around an example of alliteration in these lyrics.

2. Underline two rhythmic patterns in these lyrics.

3. Write a sentence that shows alliteration.

_____

_____

© Macmillan/McGraw-Hill

At Home: Read poetry or other rhymes with your child and have
him or her identify examples of alliteration and rhythmic patterns.

Name _____

**A. Write three words that begin with each blend
listed below.**

str   **scr**   **spr**

_____   _____   _____

_____   _____   _____

_____   _____   _____

**B. Use six of the words you wrote above to write
six sentences.**

1. _____

2. _____

3. _____

4. _____

5. _____

6. _____

At Home: Look up words that start with *scr, str,* and *spr*
in the dictionary. Invite your child to read the words and
discuss any words that are new.

Click, Clack, Moo: Cows
That Type • **Book 2.1/Unit 3**   **117**

A. Write a word from the box for each definition below.

> furious   snoop   emergency   impatient   demand   sincerely

1. to ask forcefully _____

2. not able to put up with delay or problem calmly and without

   anger _____

3. very angry _____

4. done in an honest and true way _____

5. to sneak around in order to find information

   _____

6. having to do with something important or dangerous that needs

   fast action _____

B. Use at least two words from the box to write two sentences on the lines below.

7. _____

   _____

8. _____

   _____

At Home: Invite your child to make riddles for each
vocabulary word.

© Macmillan/McGraw-Hill

**As you read *Click, Clack, Moo: Cows That Type,* fill in
the Cause and Effect Chart.**

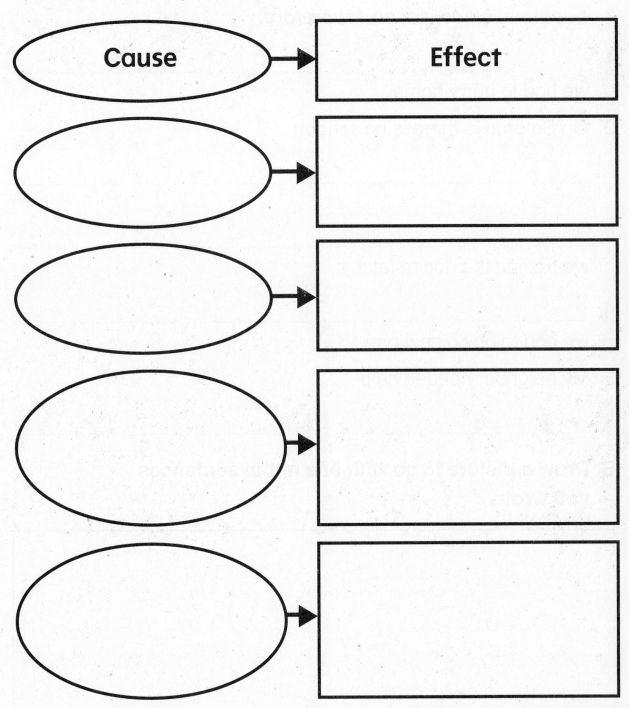

Cause → **Effect**

How does the information you wrote in this Cause and Effect Chart
help you to better understand *Click, Clack, Moo: Cows That Type*?

At Home: Have your child use the chart to retell the story.

Click, Clack, Moo: Cows
That Type • **Book 2.1/Unit 3**

119

A. Write a cause or an effect to complete each sentence. Use words that signal a cause such as *if, then, because, since, so,* and *therefore*.

1. _____

we had to hurry home.

2. On Saturdays there is no school

_____

3. _____

we trained the dog to fetch it.

4. _____

we had to buy a new one.

5. My neighbor needed help

_____

B. Draw a picture to go with one of the sentences you wrote.

At Home: As you read with your child, make a game of finding the cause and effect relationships in stories.

© Macmillan/McGraw-Hill

As I read I will pay attention to and copy intonation, emphasis, and tempo.

	Mrs. Periwinkle's country store stood at the end
8	of Cherry Blossom Lane.
12	It was famous for the beautiful knitted woolens sold there.
22	If you were to **snoop** around the store, you would see
33	Mrs. Periwinkle. She would be scrubbing, sweeping, or knitting.
42	One morning Mrs. Periwinkle was dusting and fussing even
51	more than usual.
54	Her new helper was about to arrive at the store.
64	Clip-clop-trip-trop went the sound of hooves up the pebbled path.
77	"She's here!" Mrs. Periwinkle hung up her duster, then flung
87	open the front door.
91	She bounced down the path, eager to greet Angora.
100	"Welcome, Angora," said Mrs. Periwinkle. "Come inside." 107

Comprehension Check

1. Why was Mrs. Periwinkle working so hard to clean up her store? **Cause and Effect**

2. Where is this scene taking place? **Character and Setting**

	Words Read	−	Number of Errors	=	Words Correct Score
First Read		−		=	
Second Read		−		=	

At Home: Help your child read the passage, paying attention to the goal at the top of the page.

Click, Clack, Moo: Cows That Type • **Book 2.1/Unit 3**

A. Look at the thesaurus entry. Then read each sentence below. Figure out which meaning of *high* is used in the sentence and write its number on the line.

high *adjective* **1.** Having great height. *The mountains are **high**.* tall, lofty, towering **2.** Greater than others in importance, amount, or size. *Tim got a **high** score on that game.* top, peak, maximum **3.** Describing a sharp sound. *I heard the bird's **high** chirps in the morning.* sharp, shrill, piercing

1. He stacked the blocks so high. ____

2. The high notes were hard to sing. ____

3. She had a high test score. ____

4. He has a high position with the company. ____

5. That nest is high on the cliff. ____

6. My dog can hear high notes. ____

B. Write a sentence that uses a synonym for *high*.
Then tell which definition you used in your sentence.

_____

_____

_____

_____

At Home: Help your child find a few words he or she already knows well. Then help him or her think of synonyms. Discuss the ways in which the synonyms are alike and different.

© Macmillan/McGraw-Hill

Write five sentences. In each sentence use a singular possessive noun and a word that has a *scr-*, *spr-*, or *str-* blend. Use each consonant blend at least once.

1. _____

_____

2. _____

_____

3. _____

_____

4. _____

_____

5. _____

_____

At Home: Have your child practice writing possessives using the names of people and objects in your home. Then ask him or her to use the possessives in a sentence.

Click, Clack, Moo: Cows That Type • **Book 2.1/Unit 3** 123

**Look at each calendar. Finish filling in all the dates.
Then write an answer to each question below.**

FEBRUARY						
SUN.	MON.	TUE.	WED.	THUR.	FRI.	SAT.
	1	2	3	4	5	6
7	8	9	10	11	12	13
14	15	16	17	18	19	20

MARCH						
SUN.	MON.	TUE.	WED.	THUR.	FRI.	SAT.
	1	2	3	4	5	6
7	8	9	10	11	12	13
14	15	16	17	18	19	20

1. Name two ways the two months are alike.

_____

_____

2. Pick any Tuesday. Color it blue. Count 5 more days. Color the
fifth day yellow. What day of the week is the yellow day?

_____

3. Which month is more like the other months of the year? Why?

_____

_____

4. If today is February 25, how many days is it until March 3?

_____

5. Which month has more Mondays?

_____

At Home: Help your child read a calendar. Have him or her
find today's date and the dates of any upcoming events.
Figure out how many days until each event.

A. Write the synonym from the box for the underlined word in each sentence.

sincerely	perform	remember
accident	impatient	frantically

1. Did you <u>recall</u> my birthday? _____

2. Lee gets <u>restless</u> when standing in long lines.

   _____

3. I will <u>present</u> a song for you. _____

4. In the <u>disaster</u> I scraped my elbow. _____

5. They <u>wildly</u> searched for the lost dog. _____

6. Danny <u>truly</u> apologized. _____

B. Match each word to its *antonym*. Write the letter on the line.

1. delicious ____   **a.** deny

2. furious ____   **b.** gross

3. unable ____   **c.** rebels

4. confirm ____   **d.** ashamed

5. proud ____   **e.** capable

6. obeys ____   **f.** delighted

A. These words have more than one meaning. Draw a line from each word to two different meanings.

1. leaves

2. strike

3. pupil

4. watch

5. rash

a. not careful

b. to observe

c. the black center of your eye

d. to hit

e. green parts growing from the stem of a plant

f. the call when the batter misses a pitch

g. goes away

h. an itchy, red patch of skin

i. a clock worn on the wrist

j. a student

B. Write the definition for each word. Then use the word in a sentence. Write it on the line.

1. gasped _____

_____

2. enormous _____

_____

3. ancient _____

_____

Study the code. Then use the code to write the correct word that completes each sentence.

a	b	d	e	f	g	h	k
1	2	3	4	5	6	7	8

l	n	o	p	r	s	t	y
9	10	11	12	13	14	15	16

1. Megan was [2, 11, 13, 10] _____ in June.

2. The opposite of south is [10, 11, 13, 15, 7] _____.

3. The [14, 15, 1, 13] _____ was shining brightly.

4. Polly ate her salad with a [5, 11, 13, 8] _____.

5. Rachel bought some [16, 1, 13, 10] _____ to knit.

6. Keith rode a [7, 11, 13, 14, 4] _____ through the meadow.

7. Three feet equals one [16, 1, 13, 3] _____.

8. Be careful, the pencil point is very [14, 7, 1, 13, 12]

_____.

At Home: Help your child name a rhyming word for each *r*-controlled word above.

A. Use a word from the box to solve each riddle.

| itches | puddles | handy | preen | beasts | nibble |

1. These are filled with water. If you step in them, your feet will get wet.

   _____

2. You do this to take small bites of food.

   _____

3. These are wild animals. Some may be afraid of them.

   _____

4. This describes something that is helpful. It means the opposite of useless.

   _____

B. Write a riddle or a sentence for each word you did not use.

5. _____

   _____

6. _____

   _____

Name _____

**As you read *Splish! Splash! Animal Baths*, fill in the
Compare and Contrast Chart.**

Animal	Animal	Animal
Behavior	**Behavior**	**Behavior**

How does the information you wrote in this Compare and Contrast
Chart help you to better understand *Splish! Splash! Animal Baths*?

© Macmillan/McGraw-Hill

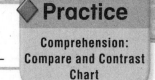

At Home: Have your child use the chart to retell the story.

Splish! Splash! Animal Baths
Book 2.2/Unit 4
129

**Choose two animals, one land animal and one water
animal. Write their names on the lines. Write a paragraph
that explains how the animals are alike. Then write a
paragraph that explains how they are different.**

_____   _____

Alike

_____

_____

_____

_____

Different

_____

_____

_____

_____

At Home: Have your child draw a picture of the two
animals. Then have him or her write some of the things that
he or she remembers about the animals.

© Macmillan/McGraw-Hill

Name _____

As I read, I will pay attention to the punctuation in each sentence.

	Sloths eat, sleep, and even have babies upside down. They
10	use their huge claws to hang from high branches in trees.
21	They can sleep up to 20 hours a day while hanging!
31	Sloths live in the rain forests of Central and South America.
42	Rain forests are very warm, wet forests. It rains there almost
53	every day. Rain forests are homes to millions of plants and
64	animals.
65	Sloths are nocturnal. They sleep during the day and are
75	active at night. But even when they are moving, sloths are still
87	the slowest mammal on Earth. 92

Comprehension Check

1. How are sloths unique among mammals? **Compare and Contrast**

2. Where do sloths live? When are they awake? **Character and Setting**

	Words Read	–	Number of Errors	=	Words Correct Score
First Read		–		=	
Second Read		–		=	

© Macmillan/McGraw-Hill

At Home: Help your child read the passage, paying attention to the goal at the top of the page.

Splish! Splash! Animal Baths
Book 2.2/Unit 4

131

Name _____

A. Write a story about going to the zoo. It can be a non-fiction or fiction. Tell about the animals you saw and what they did or ate. Also include the things that you did and who you went with to the zoo.

Title: _____

_____

_____

_____

_____

_____

_____

_____

B. Now, go back and circle each noun that ends with *s* or *–es*.

© Macmillan/McGraw-Hill

At Home: Have your child read his or her story aloud. Invite him or her to count how many inflected nouns appear in the story.

Name _____

A. Read the clues and write a word to fit each description.

1. Write two, one syllable words that have *ar* in them.

_____   _____

2. Write two, one syllable words that have *or* in them.

_____   _____

3. Write two, two syllable words that have *ar* in them.

_____   _____

4. Write two, two syllable words that have *or* in them.

_____   _____

5. Write two, three syllable words that have *ar* in them.

_____   _____

6. Write two, three syllable words that have *or* in them.

_____   _____

B. Write a slash to separate the syllables.

7. popular   **8.** grasshopper

9. mailbox   **10.** kangaroo

At Home: Have your child write a short story and
point out the two-syllable and three-syllable words.

Splish! Splash! Animal Baths

133

Book 2.2/Unit 4

Write a short play. Create four characters and an interesting setting. Write the play on the lines.

Characters:

_____ _____ _____ _____

Setting: _____

_____

_____

_____

_____

_____

_____

_____

_____

At Home: Have your child read his or her play with someone at home. Have him or her assign a character for each person to read.

Find the words from the box in the puzzle. Then write each word in the correct column below.

| turn | first | verse | fur | term | stir |
| her | sir | surf | clerk | thirst | spur |

```
d   s   u   r   f   s   p   u   r   b
v   h   t   u   r   n   i   h   k   o
l   g   e   i   b   k   j   r   l   t
y   e   r   a   r   y   u   q   d   h
c   x   m   p   b   f   l   e   s   i
l   r   d   r   y   i   g   s   q   r
e   c   e   f   t   r   p   r   z   s
r   h   g   q   c   s   d   e   g   t
k   s   r   w   v   t   c   v   t   f
```

words with *ir*	words with *er*	words with *ur*
1. _____	5. _____	9. _____
2. _____	6. _____	10. _____
3. _____	7. _____	11. _____
4. _____	8. _____	12. _____

© Macmillan/McGraw-Hill

At Home: Have your child write a poem using at least four
words that have the /ur/ sound spelled er, ir, or ur.

Goose's Story • **Book 2.2/Unit 4** 135

Name _____

Read each word below. Find its synonym or antonym in the box. Then use each word from the box in a sentence. Write it on the lines.

wider   saddest   freezes   imagine   deserted   balance

1. narrower _____

_____

2. picture _____

_____

3. happiest _____

_____

4. stability _____

_____

5. abandoned _____

_____

6. boils _____

_____

Name _____

As you read *Goose's Story*, fill in the Cause and
Effect Chart.

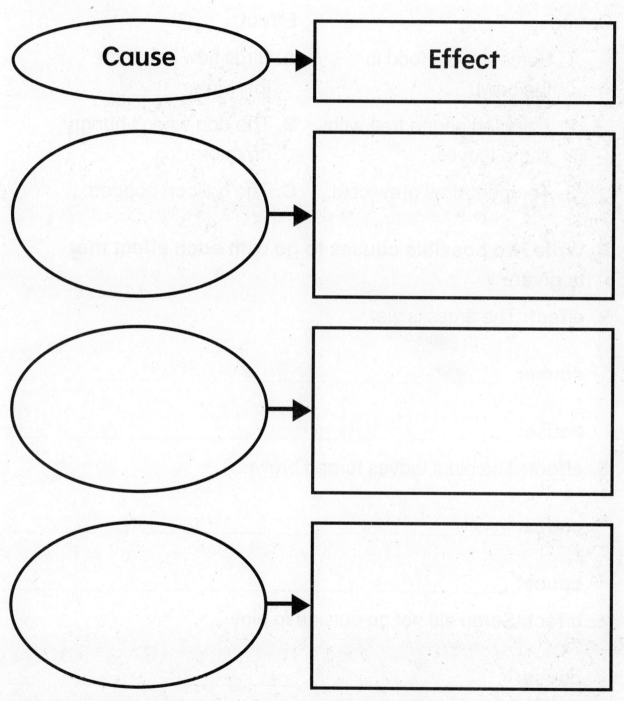

How does the information you wrote in this Cause and Effect Chart
help you to better understand *Goose's Story*?

At Home: Have your child use the chart to retell the story.

Goose's Story • **Book 2.2/Unit 4** 137

© Macmillan/McGraw-Hill

A. Match each cause in the first column with its effect in the second column. Write the letter of the effect on the line.

Cause

___ **1.** Someone put food in the bowl.

___ **2.** It floated near a tree with sharp leaves.

___ **3.** Temperatures grew cold.

Effect

A. Birds flew south for the winter.

B. The dog wasn't hungry anymore.

C. The balloon popped.

B. Write two possible causes to go with each effect that is given.

4. effect: The grass is wet.

cause:_____

cause:_____

5. effect: The plant leaves turned brown.

cause:_____

cause:_____

6. effect: Sarah did not go outside to play.

cause:_____

cause:_____

© Macmillan/McGraw-Hill

At Home: With your child, say the *Humpty Dumpty* rhyme. Ask how a mother bird might care for an egg in real life to keep it from falling out of a nest.

As I read, I will pay attention to the punctuation in each sentence.

	"Catch him!" Lindy shouted.
4	The monkey jumped on top of the boxes. It tried to balance,
16	but it could not. Crash! The boxes fell to the ground. The
28	monkey landed safely.
31	It was another day in the animal rescue center. Lindy's
41	mom picked up the monkey.
46	"It's good that it's jumping around," said Lindy's mom.
55	"That means its broken leg is healing. Soon we'll be able to
67	take it back to the wild where it belongs."
76	The animal rescue center was in the African grasslands,
85	which were an hour from the nearest town. Lindy's mom
95	was a doctor for the animals. They needed care all day and
107	night, so Lindy and her mom lived in a home next to the
120	center. Lindy couldn't **imagine** living anywhere more fun. 128

Comprehension Check

1. Why was the monkey at the animal rescue center? **Cause and Effect**

2. How does Lindy feel about living next to the rescue center? **Make Inferences**

	Words Read	–	Number of Errors	=	Words Correct Score
First Read		–		=	
Second Read		–		=	

 At Home: Help your child read the passage, paying attention to the goal at the top of the page.

Name _____

**Write a sentence about animals for each word. Then draw
a picture to go with your sentence.**

1. taller _____

   _____

2. deepest _____

   _____

3. smaller _____

   _____

4. highest _____

   _____

Name _____

Use at least four words from the box to write a paragraph about animal survival. Circle the letters that spell the *r*-controlled vowel sound in each word that you use from the box.

bird	hibernate	survive	thirst	burrows
water	dirt	fur	surroundings	shelter

_____

_____

_____

_____

_____

_____

_____

_____

At Home: Together with your child, read a story. Ask him or her to point out words that have the /ur/ sound spelled with *er, ir,* or *ur.*

Goose's Story • **Book 2.2/Unit 4** ◆141◆

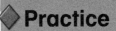
Read the map and answer the questions below.

Town Map

1. What is south of Main Street? _____

2. What is on the northeast side of Grand Avenue? _____

_____

3. What direction would you have to travel to get from the school

to the police station? _____

4. What is south of the library but north of Main Street? _____

_____

5. What is on the southwest side of Grand Avenue? _____

At Home: Ask your child to draw a new map based on these directions: The park is next to the school. The bank is north of the park. A lake is south of the park.

Name _____

A. Circle the word in each sentence that has the same vowel sound you hear in the words *could* and *shook*. Then write a word that has the same vowel sound and spelling as the word you circled.

Why We
Should
Recycle

1. This book is about
   recycling.   _____

2. Tina spread wood chips
   around the garden.   _____

3. We should turn off the
   lights when we leave.   _____

4. It is good to save water.   _____

5. Paco took his trash to
   the bin.   _____

6. Would you help me
   clean up this park?   _____

B. Write two sentences about recycling. Use two of the words you circled and wrote above.

7. _____

8. _____

At Home: Challenge your child to make a crossword puzzle using some of the words he or she circled and wrote.

A. Read each sentence. Write *T* if the sentence is true.
Write *F* if the sentence is false.

____ **1.** The foods an animal eats are its **remains**.

____ **2.** You should waste water if you care about **conservation**.

____ **3.** It is good to help a friend who is in **trouble**.

____ **4.** A pillow is the **hardest** thing in your house.

____ **5.** **Conservation** of water is good for the Earth.

____ **6.** **Extinct** animals can be found living near your home.

____ **7.** The **remains** of a bird that has died could include bones and feathers.

____ **8.** Most people enjoy having **trouble**.

B. Write two sentences that correct false statements above.

9. _____

_____

10. _____

_____

Name _____

As you read *A Way to Help Planet Earth*, fill in the
Description Web.

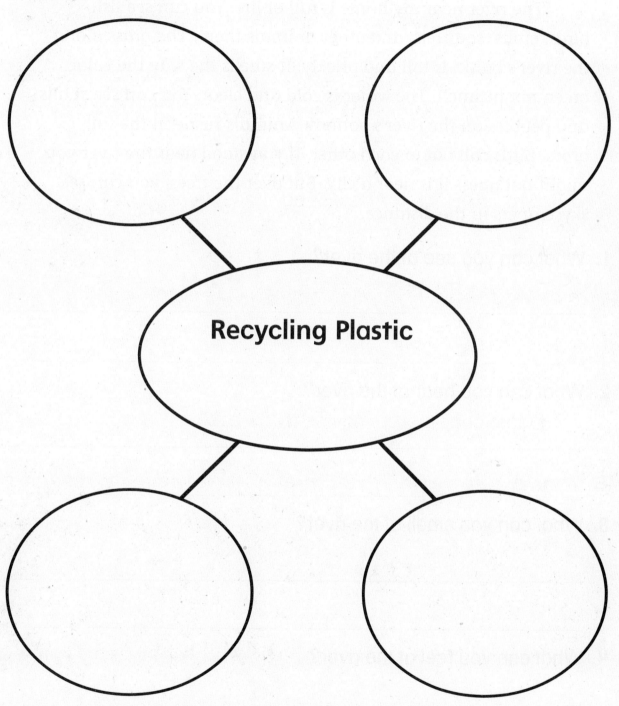

Recycling Plastic

How does the information you wrote in this Description Web help
you to better understand *A Way to Help Planet Earth*?

© Macmillan/McGraw-Hill

At Home: Have your child use the chart to retell the story.

A Way to Help Planet Earth
Book 2.2/Unit 4

145

Name _____

Read the description. Then answer the questions.

The river near my home is full of life. You can see fish, birds, crabs, squirrels, and other animals there. The grass along the river's banks is tall and prickly. It smells the way the color green might smell. The water is cold and clear. You can see snails and pebbles on the river's bottom. Animals rustle in the tall grass. Birds call out to each other. If you stood near the river you might not guess it is near a city. But over the trees, you can see skyscrapers in the distance.

1. What can you see at the river?

_____

_____

2. What can you hear at the river?

_____

_____

3. What can you smell at the river?

_____

_____

4. What can you feel at the river?

_____

_____

At Home: Have your child give a short description of a place he or she has seen but you have not. Ask questions about how it looks, sounds, smells, and feels.

A. Read the paragraph. Then answer the questions.

On Earth Day, some kids in Ms. Lansing's class did a lot. Others did almost nothing. Kendra ran a cleanup of the school grounds. She got lots of kids from every grade to pick up trash. Kendra also ran a bake sale. She raised a lot of money. She sent the money to a group that saves rain forests. Percy read about recycling on the Internet. Then he wrote a list of things kids can recycle. Carlos did the least for Earth Day. He did just one little thing. He made sure to put his juice box in the right bin after lunch.

1. Which kid was **busiest** on Earth Day? _____

2. Underline the context clues that helped you figure out the answer to question 1.

3. Which kid was the **laziest** on Earth Day? _____

4. Draw a circle around the context clues that helped you figure out the answer to question 3.

5. Which kid was **busier** than Carlos but not as busy as Kendra? _____

B. Write a few sentences comparing a group of three or more things or animals.

6. _____

_____

_____

At Home: Put three household items of different sizes in a row. Have your child write sentences that compare the items *without* using adjectives that end in-*er* or -*est*.

A Way to Help Planet Earth
Book 2.2/Unit 4
147

© Macmillan/McGraw-Hill

Look at the article below. Then follow the directions.

Caring for Earth's Habitats

How can we care for the water?
Keep water clean by picking up trash.
How can we care for the air?
Ride bikes and walk.
How can we care for the land?
Plant trees and recycle.
More ways to help care for Earth can
be found in the book *What I Can Do to Help*.

_____

_____

_____

1. Underline the title of the article.

2. Draw a circle around the words that are in bold type. Then explain why these words are in bold type.

_____

_____

3. Draw a box around the words that are in italic type. Then explain why these words are in italic type.

_____

_____

4. What information is shown in the sidebar? _____

5. Write a caption under the picture.

 At Home: Look through magazines and newspapers with your child. Point out examples of the text features and have him or her identify them and explain their purpose.

As I read, I will pay attention to the pronunciation of vocabulary words.

	In 1986 the Pan African (which means "all of Africa") Green
10	Belt Movement was started. Wangari's good idea keeps spreading.
19	Many other countries now have groups who plant trees and help
30	people in villages. But a lot **remains** to be done.
40	Wangari Maathai's idea was so good that she won a
50	Nobel Peace Prize in 2004. The Nobel Peace Prize voting committee
60	said about Wangari, "She thinks globally and acts locally."
69	Wangari was proud to get the award. "It is not my own prize
82	but for the entire country," she said. "And I'm told the whole of
95	Africa is celebrating."
98	Wangari was also named "one of the 100 heroines of the
108	world" by a United Nations group. Her simple idea grew into
119	great action. It is helping with **conservation** and making people's
129	lives better. 131

Comprehension Check

1. What is the Pan African Green Belt movement? **Description**

2. When did Wangari say, "I'm told all of Africa is celebrating"?
Sequence

	Words Read	–	Number of Errors	=	Words Correct Score
First Read		–		=	
Second Read		–		=	

© Macmillan/McGraw-Hill

At Home: Help your child read the passage, paying attention to the goal at the top of the page.

A Way to Help Planet Earth
Book 2.2/Unit 4
149

Name _____

A. Rewrite each word. Put hyphens (-) between the syllables. The first one is done for you.

1. blackberry   **black-ber-ry**

2. hooked   _____

3. watchful   _____

4. hooded   _____

5. neighborhood   _____

6. suppose   _____

7. overlooking   _____

8. unsafely   _____

B. Use syllables from the box to fill in the blanks and form words.

der	mem	stood	peck	un
wood	ber	er	re	

9. ___ ___ + ___ ___ ___ + ___ ___ ___

10. ___ ___ + ___ ___ ___ + ___ ___ ___

11. ___ ___ ___ + ___ ___ ___ + ___ ___

12. ___ ___ + ___ ___ ___ ___ + ___ ___ ___

 At Home: Look through a book or newspaper and point out words to your child. Have him or her say how many syllables each word has, then rewrite the word, breaking it into syllables.

© Macmillan/McGraw-Hill

Name _____

| boom | cool | blew | grew | true |
| blue | fruit | rainsuits | shoes | canoe |

Write a silly newspaper article about a big storm and draw a picture for it. Use at least five of the words from the box in your article. Include a title, your name, and a caption for the picture. Circle the words from the box that you used in your story.

_____

_____

_____

_____

_____

_____

_____

_____

© Macmillan/McGraw-Hill

At Home: Have your child look for words with the letters *oo, ui, ew, oe,* and *ue* in the newspaper. Help him or her list and read the words.

Super Storms • Book 2.2/Unit 4 151

Read the clues. Write the answers in the puzzle.

> beware   destroy   grasslands   prevent   uprooted   violent

Down

1. to stop from happening

2. pulled up by the roots

3. to ruin or make useless

Across

4. lands covered with grass, often used as pasture

5. happening with or because of strong force

6. to be on guard against

As you read *Super Storms*, fill in the Predictions Chart.

What I Predict	What Happens

© Macmillan/McGraw-Hill

How does the information you wrote in this Predictions Chart help you to better understand *Super Storms*?

At Home: Have your child use the chart to retell the story.

Super Storms • **Book 2.2/Unit 4** ◆153◆

Read the story. Draw a picture that shows what might happen next. Then write your prediction and ending to the story on the lines below.

It was the worst storm to hit in the last twelve months. Dangerous winds whipped through the park. Tree branches littered the paths. Garbage cans overturned and trash flew everywhere. Luckily no one was hurt, but a few bird nests were ripped from the trees. Pieces of broken eggshells lay shattered on the ground. Park workers and volunteers stood and looked at the damage.

_____

_____

_____

_____

_____

© Macmillan/McGraw-Hill

 At Home: Have your child tell you about his or her day. Then ask him or her to predict something that might happen tomorrow.

As I read, I will pay attention to tempo and the pronunciation of the vocabulary words.

	The wind began to howl. Long blades of grass swished
10	and swayed.
12	They watched as a bush broke free of its roots. It flew
24	through the air and landed on the dirt.
32	"This is wild," Juan said. "The wind just **uprooted** that bush!"
43	Pedro turned his horse toward home. "Everyone, home! Now!"
52	he yelled.
54	Shadow was upset. Juan watched as a bolt of lightning split
65	the sky in two. The sky grew dark.
73	Luisa rubbed Sadie's neck to calm her. Then she looked at
84	Juan and Shadow. Luisa could see the whites of Shadow's
96	eyes, which were wide with fear.
100	They heard a noise that sounded like the stomach rumble
110	of a hungry giant. **Violent** thunder cracked around them. 119

Comprehension Check

1. What is happening with the weather? **Draw Conclusions**

2. What are Sadie and Shadow? **Make Inferences**

	Words Read	–	Number of Errors	=	Words Correct Score
First Read		–		=	
Second Read		–		=	

At Home: Help your child read the passage, paying attention to the goal at the top of the page.

Super Storms • Book 2.2/Unit 4   155

© Macmillan/McGraw-Hill

Name _____

A. Write a smaller word next to each word below to make compound words.

I. back_____ 2. back_____ 3. back_____

4. down_____ 5. down_____ 6. down_____

7. _____body 8. _____body 9. _____body

10. _____light II. _____light 12. _____light

13. home_____ 14. home_____ 15. home_____

16. snow_____ 17. snow_____ 18. snow_____

B. Write four sentences using the compound words you wrote.

19. _____

20. _____

21. _____

22. _____

© Macmillan/McGraw-Hill

At Home: Help your child find five compound words in a magazine or book. Have him or her use the words in sentences.

Use some of the words in the box to finish the story. Tell how Mr. Loop's class will raise the money to help others. Then circle the story words that have the vowel sounds you hear in the words *cool*, *fruit*, *new*, *clue* and *shoe*.

food	school	few	new	blue
glue	fruit	suit	shoes	canoe

Mr. Loop's class raises money to help others who need it. This year his new class will help the victims of a recent typhoon. The typhoon struck Southeast Asia last Monday at noon.

Mr. Loop _____

_____

_____

_____

At Home: Have your child talk about a favorite activity. List all the words used with the /oo/ sound. Then have him or her make a chart with each word.

Super Storms • Book 2.2/Unit 4 157

**Read the words to this nursery rhyme. Then answer
the questions below.**

> Willie boy , Willie boy,
> Where are you going?
> Oh, let us go with you
> This sunshiny day.
>
> I'm going to the meadow
> To see them a-mowing.
> I'm going to help the girls
> Turn the new hay.

I. What words are repeated in this rhyme? _____

_____

2. What is the mood in this rhyme? _____

3. Which words or lines help create that mood? _____

_____

_____

4. Write your own short poem on the lines below. Include
repetition and words that give your poem a certain mood.

_____

_____

_____

© Macmillan/McGraw-Hill

At Home: Read other poems and rhymes with your child.
Talk about the use of repetition and the words a poet
chooses to create a mood.

Name _____

Make up a silly story about going on a camping trip by answering one of the questions below. Use at least four words from the box. Write the story on the lines.

| because | claw | cause | hawk | squawk | haul |
| fawn | caught | saw | autumn | dawn | yawn |

a. What happened when you saw a hawk's nest in the tree right next to your tent?

b. What happened when a fawn, or a young deer, and its mother got really close to your campsite?

_____

_____

_____

_____

_____

_____

_____

At Home: Write words with a variety of vowels sounds, including *au* and *aw* words, on index cards. Shuffle the cards and have your child sort them by vowel sound.

Nutik, the Wolf Pup • Book 2.2/Unit 4　159

Name _____

Use the code to figure out what the vocabulary word is.
Write it on the line. Then follow the directions.

Code

A	B	C	D	E	F	G	H	I	J	K	L	M
1	2	3	4	5	6	7	8	9	10	11	12	13

N	O	P	Q	R	S	T	U	V	W	X	Y	Z
14	15	16	17	18	19	20	21	22	23	24	25	26

1. 7-12-1-14-3-5-4   Write an antonym for this word.

_____

2. 7-12-5-1-13-5-4   Write a synonym for this word.

_____

3. 2-5-12-15-22-5-4   Write an antonym for this word.

_____

4. 16-18-15-13-9-19-5-4   Write a synonym for this word.

_____

5. 23-9-7-7-12-5-4   Write a synonym for this word.

_____

6. 14-15-2-12-5   Write an antonym for this word.

_____

Name _____

As you read *Nutik, the Wolf Pup,* **fill in the Inference Chart.**

What I Read	What I Know

↓

My Inferences

How does the information you wrote in this Inference Chart
help you to better understand *Nutik, the Wolf Pup?*

At Home: Have your child use the chart to retell the story.

Read the passage and answer the questions below.

The Octopus

There are over 250 different kinds of octopuses. They come in many sizes, from 30 feet long to only 4 inches long. People once believed the octopus was a sea monster. They told stories about huge octopuses. People thought that octopuses pulled ships under water. Today we know that these stories were just fiction. The real octopus is a shy sea creature.

An octopus has a soft body with no outer shell. It has eight arms. Its arms are lined with strong suckers. The suckers help it hold on to rocks and other objects. Octopuses have a lot in common with snails and clams, but they are much more intelligent. Some scientists say octopuses may be as smart as dogs are.

I. Why do you think people once believed that the octopus was a

sea monster? _____

_____

_____

2. Is an octopus bigger or smaller than a snail? Explain.

_____

_____

_____

© Macmillan/McGraw-Hill

At Home: As you read, have your child tell you the things he or she "guessed" about the story.

As I read, I will pay attention and copy tone and expression.

	Grasslands are big open spaces where tall grass grows. When
10	the wind blows, grasslands look like rolling seas of grass.
20	The grasslands of Africa are famous for being full of animals.
31	Lions sometimes live and hunt here. Their cubs play hide-and-
41	seek in the tall green and brown grass.
48	There are two major types of grasslands: tropical grasslands
57	and temperate grasslands.
60	Tropical grasslands are hot all year. Most of them have heavy
71	rain in the summer. Africa has tropical grasslands.
79	Temperate grasslands have hot summers and cold winters.
87	Often there are strong winds because few trees grow there. North
98	America has a large temperate grassland area.
105	Soil is important in grasslands. Grassland soil is rich and dark.
116	This helps plants and grasses grow.
122	The grasses' roots are also important. They hold the soil
132	together. 133

Comprehension Check

1. What causes temperate grasslands to have strong winds?
Cause and Effect

2. Do you think it would be hot in a tropical grassland region in the winter? **Make and Confirm Predictions**

	Words Read	–	Number of Errors	=	Words Correct Score
First Read		–		=	
Second Read		–		=	

At Home: Help your child read the passage, paying attention to the goal at the top of the page.

Complete the sentences. Use the verb in ( ). The first sentence should tell about an action happening in the present. The second sentence should tell about an action that happened in the past.

1. (stalk)

present: The lion and her cubs _____

_____

past: The lion and her cubs _____

_____

2. (scratch)

present: The polar bear _____

_____

past: The polar bear _____

_____

3. (howl)

present: The Arctic wolf _____

_____

past: The Arctic wolf _____

_____

© Macmillan/McGraw-Hill

At Home: Have your child look through magazines and newspapers to find examples of inflected verbs.

Name _____

Read each clue. Write words with *au* and *aw* to complete the puzzle.

Across

6. groups of people who watch or listen to a show, speech, or other performance

Down

1. a synonym for *uncomfortable* or *ungraceful*

2. When the parrot is upset, it makes this noise.

3. A leaky _____ goes drip, drip, drip into the sink.

4. I want to eat _____ I am hungry.

5. what you do to a rocket to get it into space

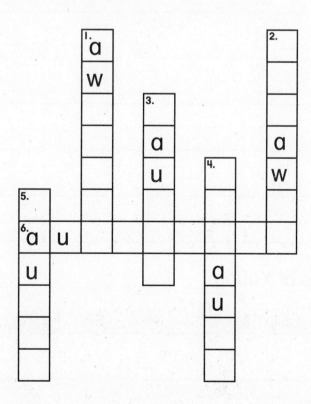

At Home: Find words that have the *au* and *aw* vowel patterns in the texts that you read together. Have your child tell you the meaning of the words you find.

Nutik, the Wolf Pup • **Book 2.2/Unit 4** ◆165◆

A. Suppose you have to write a one-page paper on one animal. Think about this research assignment as you answer each question below.

1. Write a topic that best fits the assignment. _____

2. Would an encyclopedia be a good reference source?

 Why or why not? _____

 _____

B. The encyclopedia article on your animal has sections with heads. What kinds of information would you find under each head below?

3. Appearance: _____

 _____

4. Habitat: _____

 _____

5. Diet: _____

 _____

6. Birth and Care of Young: _____

 _____

 _____

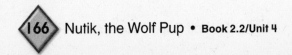

At Home: Look at different encyclopedia entries for animals with your child. Talk about how his or her answers above compare with what he or she finds in the encyclopedia.

© Macmillan/McGraw-Hill

Complete the sentences.

1. A **nurse** helps _____

2. The **violent** storm _____

3. Good **conservation** is _____

   _____

4. The **saddest** thing that I know of is _____

   _____

5. My most **beloved** toy is _____ because _____

   _____

6. The _____ **nibbles** on _____

7. When I go to a **farm**, I would like to _____

   _____

8. My **hardest** chore is _____

   _____

9. You can help **prevent** _____

   _____

10. Because of the rain, we **could** not _____

   _____

Write the word from the box that completes each sentence.

suit	extinct	itches	caught	deserted
noble	preen	grasslands	gleamed	balance

1. The poison ivy gave Audrey _____ on her leg.

2. We looked through the house, but it was _____.

3. The polished trophies _____ in the sunlight.

4. Zebras and giraffes roam the _____ of Africa.

5. The trapper _____ the monkey that escaped from the zoo.

6. The tyrannosaurus is an _____ animal.

7. The duck began to _____ to get the mud off its wings.

8. Tina had to _____ as she walked on the beam.

9. Jerry got a new _____ to wear.

10. The wolf on the hilltop looked grand and _____.

Name _____

Write a word that matches each description. (Hint: Each word has the letter pair *ow* or *ou* in it.) Then use each word in a sentence.

1. the opposite of north

_____

2. a circus performer who wears a red nose and large shoes

_____

3. what you might say if you cut your finger

_____

4. a tall building

_____

5. say something loudly

_____

6. the color of chocolate

_____

7. a cloth you use to dry yourself

_____

© Macmillan/McGraw-Hill

At Home: Have your child think of three words that have *ou* or *ow*. Then have him or her write a sentence for each one.

Dig, Wait, Listen
Book 2.2/Unit 5
169

Play this game with a partner.

1. First make a word card for each word in the box. Then write the definition of the word on the back of the card. Shuffle the cards. Put them in a pile.

2. Take turns picking a card. Read one side of the card only. Tell the meaning for the word or give the word for the meaning.

3. Keep the cards you get right. Play until there are no cards left.

4. Play again, but this time, use each word in a sentence. Write your sentences on the lines.

beyond	ranger's	lengthy	burrow	warning	distant

1. _____

2. _____

3. _____

4. _____

5. _____

6. _____

© Macmillan/McGraw-Hill

As you read *Dig, Wait, Listen: A Desert Toad's Tale,* **fill in the Author's Purpose Chart.**

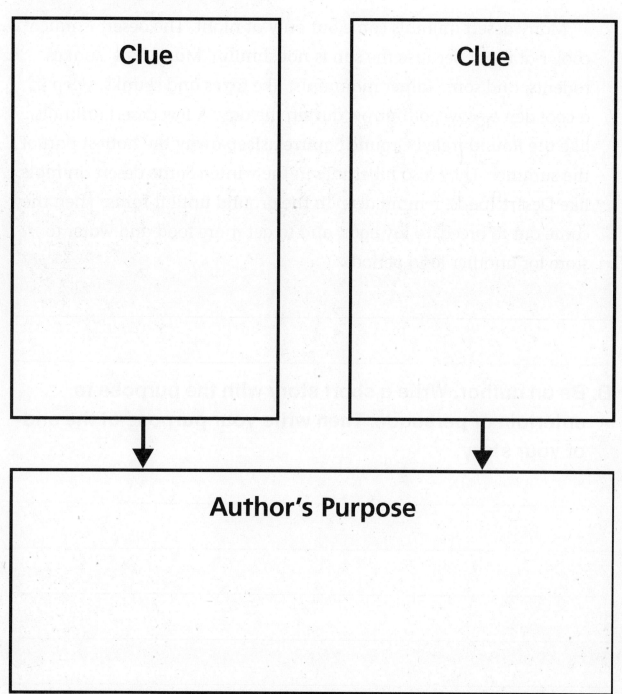

| Clue | Clue |

Author's Purpose

How does the information you wrote in this Author's Purpose Chart help you summarize *Dig, Wait, Listen: A Desert Toad's Tale?*

At Home: Have your child use the chart to retell the story.

A. Read the story below. Write a short summary that tells the author's purpose.

Many desert animals come out only at night. The desert is much cooler at night because the sun is not shining. Many bats, snakes, rodents, and some larger mammals, like foxes and skunks, sleep in a cool den or cave, or burrow during the day. A few desert animals, like the Round-tailed Ground Squirrel, sleep away the hottest part of the summer. They also hibernate in the winter. Some desert animals, like Desert Toads, remain deep in the ground until it rains. Then they come out to breed, to lay eggs, and to get more food and water to store for another long period.

_____

_____

B. Be an author. Write a short story with the purpose to entertain or persuade. Then write your purpose at the end of your story.

_____

_____

_____

_____

_____

_____

© Macmillan/McGraw-Hill

At Home: Have your child read something nonfiction and fiction. The have him or her identify the author's purpose for each selection he or she read.

As I read, I will pay attention to expression.

	Many mammals live in the Kalahari Desert. They have very
10	little water to drink. Some mammals eat only thornbushes
19	and dry grass. Others eat small rodents, bugs, and lizards.
29	Meerkats live in the Kalahari's grasslands. They are good
38	hunters that attack without warning. The meerkats eat lizards,
47	small rodents, and bugs. They even eat poisonous scorpions.
56	They bite off the scorpion's stinger, and then eat the rest.
67	Gemsboks are huge antelopes. They can live for months
76	without water. Gemsboks cool themselves down by taking
84	short quick breaths. This helps them to keep their heads cool,
95	even when their bodies are hot.
101	Gemsboks live in parts of the desert that have grass and
112	trees. They eat grass and will dig for plant roots to eat.
124	Many desert animals move slowly. That makes hunting
132	easy for lions and cheetahs.
137	Lions live in groups of twelve or fewer lions. 146

Comprehension Check

1. What is the author's main topic? **Author's Purpose**

2. How is a meerkat's diet different from a gemsbok's? **Compare and Contrast**

	Words Read	–	Number of Errors	=	Words Correct Score
First Read		–		=	
Second Read		–		=	

© Macmillan/McGraw-Hill

At Home: Help your child read the passage, paying attention to the goal at the top of the page.

Dig, Wait, Listen
Book 2.2/Unit 5

173

**Look at the picture. Use the clues in the picture to write a
story about the desert. Use the possessives in the box .**

| rabbit's | toad's | boy's | man's |

Title: _____

_____

_____

_____

_____

_____

 At Home: Have your child tell another story based on the
picture above.

Read the words in the box. Write a synonym and an antonym for each word in the correct column.

1. happy	2. shout	3. loud	4. large	5. town
6. cold	7. tall	8. now	9. old	10. fast

Synonym   **Antonym**

1. _____   _____

2. _____   _____

3. _____   _____

4. _____   _____

5. _____   _____

6. _____   _____

7. _____   _____

8. _____   _____

9. _____   _____

10. _____   _____

© Macmillan/McGraw-Hill

At Home: Have your child tell you other synonyms and antonyms for each word in the box.

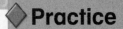
Read the paragraph. Write information from the paragraph to complete the chart.

Desert Animals

Jack rabbits, hedgehogs, and rattlesnakes are three animals that live in the desert. Jackrabbits have long ears and powerful legs. They eat grass, leaves, and twigs. Hedgehogs have spiky spines. They eat insects, mice, lizards, and eggs. Rattlesnakes have scaly skin and a rattle on their tail. They eat lizards and small animals.

Desert Animals		
Animal	**Characteristics**	**What They Eat**

 At Home: Have your child research a desert animal and write a short report. Then have him or her put that information in a chart.

A. Make new words, but keep the letters that stand for the vowel sound. Fill in each blank as you add or change letters to make the new word. The new words you will make are in the box.

| coin | royal | soil | toy | point | noise |

Example:

oil __b__ oil <u>b</u>oil

1. join

___ oin ___

2. foil

___ oi ___

3. coil

___ oil

4. boy

___ oy

5. joy

___ oy ___ ___

6. voice

___ oi ___ e

B. Use at least two of the words above in a short paragraph that tells about putting on a play.

_____

_____

_____

_____

At Home: Have your child tell you five words that rhyme with the words from the box. Then have him or her write a sentence for each new word.

Pushing Up the Sky
Book 2.2/Unit 5

177

A. Circle the words from the box in the word search puzzle.

| jabbing | agreed | randomly | signal | gathered |

a   g   a   t   h   e   r   e   d   h

g   a   m   g   u   r   e   p   i   p

r   t   j   a   b   b   i   n   g   t

e   k   s   o   j   d   t   q   h   x

e   l   a   n   g   i   s   l   b   u

d   r   a   n   d   o   m   l   y   b

B. Use three of the words in sentences that tell something about writing a play.

1. _____

_____

2. _____

_____

3. _____

_____

Name _____

As you read *Pushing Up the Sky*, fill in the
Problem and Solution Chart.

┌───┐
│   │
│   **Problem**   │
│   │
│   │
│   │
└───┘
                        ↓
┌───┐
│   │
│   **Steps to Solution**   │
│   │
│   │
│   │
│   │
│   │
│   │
│   │
└───┘
                        ↓
┌───┐
│   │
│   **Solution**   │
│   │
│   │
│   │
└───┘

How does the information you wrote in this Problem and Solution
Chart help you to better understand *Pushing Up the Sky*?

At Home: Have your child use the chart to retell the story.

Name _____

Read each problem or solution. Write a missing problem or solution that makes sense.

1. **Problem:** Pat has to spend time doing a project for school. She wants to go see a movie with friends.

   Solution: _____

   _____

2. **Problem:** _____

   _____

   Solution: The school held a bake sale so they could make more money for the club.

3. **Problem:** There were not enough children to fill all the parts in the play.

   Solution: _____

   _____

4. **Problem:** _____

   _____

   Solution: They saved their money for many weeks.

At Home: Ask your child to tell you two possible solutions for this problem: A child wants to play on a sports team. He or she has drama club at the same time practices are.

© Macmillan/McGraw-Hill

As I read, I will pay attention and copy tone and expression.

	Narrator: This play is from an old folk tale. It takes place a
13	long, long time ago. It's a tale about the sun, the moon, and
26	some of the stars in the sky.
33	It was daytime, and the Moon was trying to rest. But some of
46	her children were making a lot of noise. The Moon's children
57	were stars.
59	**Moon:** Come and rest, children!
64	**Star Children:** Not yet, Mother! We are playing in the sky.
75	**Moon:** You should not be twinkling during the day, children.
85	You should rest. You have to sparkle tonight!
93	**Star Children:** But we want to play, Mother. We like the
104	daytime. We can see our father as he shines!
113	**Narrator:** The Star Children's father was the Sun.
121	**Moon:** Then I will tell your father when he comes home that
133	you were not good.
137	**Narrator:** That evening, their Sun Father came home. 145

Comprehension Check

1. How are the sun, moon, and stars like a family in the play? **Character and Setting**

2. Why do the children want to stay outside? **Main Idea and Details**

	Words Read	–	Number of Errors	=	Words Correct Score
First Read		–		=	
Second Read		–		=	

© Macmillan/McGraw-Hill

At Home: Help your child read the passage, paying attention to the goal at the top of the page.

Name _____

A. Add the endings *-ly*, *-ed*, or *-ing* to the base words
to make as many words as you can. Make spelling
changes if you need to.

free	quick	grab	slow	try	neat
clear	quiet	safe	clap	dance	loud

_____

_____

_____

_____

_____

B. Use at least three of the words in three sentences to tell
what people watching a play often do.

I. _____

2. _____

3. _____

At Home: Ask your child to add the endings *-ly*, *-ed*, and
-ing to the word *slow* and to use each word to tell you a
short story.

© Macmillan/McGraw-Hill

A. Proofread the following flyer. Cross out each word that is used or spelled incorrectly. Write the correct word above it.

Please come too try out for the school play. It's about a girl and

a boi whose family wants to bye a ship. The family wants to sale

around the world. Their are ate people in the family.

We want to poynt out that you must be on time to try out for

the play. Joyn us in the school auditorium at won o'clock.

We think we will be threw in about one our . We hope to see

you they're!

B. Read the words. Write a homophone for each one.

1. bare _____

2. for _____

3. road _____

4. weak _____

At Home: Have your child use the words *sent, scent,* and *cent* in a silly sentence that shows the correct meaning for each word.

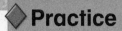
Imagine that you are a writer for an entertainment magazine. You are going to interview your favorite actor or singer.

1. Who would you interview? Why?

_____

_____

2. Write three questions you would ask this person.

_____

_____

_____

3. Why would an interview be a good way to get the answers to these questions?

_____

_____

4. Why do you think people read interviews?

_____

_____

At Home: Have your child find and read examples of interviews in magazines.

© Macmillan/McGraw-Hill

A. Find ten words that begin or end with the schwa sound in the word puzzle below. Circle the words as you find them.

```
q z a b o u t d g v t a
e e f r t c d w o k g i
k b b t j x o p k l m r
a r n f a e h m u a d d
w a z z i p n s m v b s
a x c j g a p y k a l o
z c a h e a d l b l g f
a o p t r t r p e i k a
c m a m a g h b m k n v
r q n i a g a d d e w s
```

B. Choose five of the words you circled above. Write a sentence for each word on the lines below.

1. _____

2. _____

3. _____

4. _____

5. _____

At Home: Work with your child to think of a few more two-syllable words that begin or end with an unstressed *a* sound.

Name _____

A. Choose a word from the box to match each clue. Write the word on the line.

areas	oceans	planet	vast	voyage

1. These are huge bodies of salt water. _____

2. This is a long trip by sea, air, or land. _____

3. This is a large object in space that travels around the Sun.

    _____

4. These are places, or sections of a place. _____

5. This word tells about something huge. _____

B. Write a paragraph using all five words from the box.

_____

_____

_____

_____

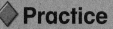
As you read *Columbus Explores New Lands*, fill in the Main Idea and Details Web.

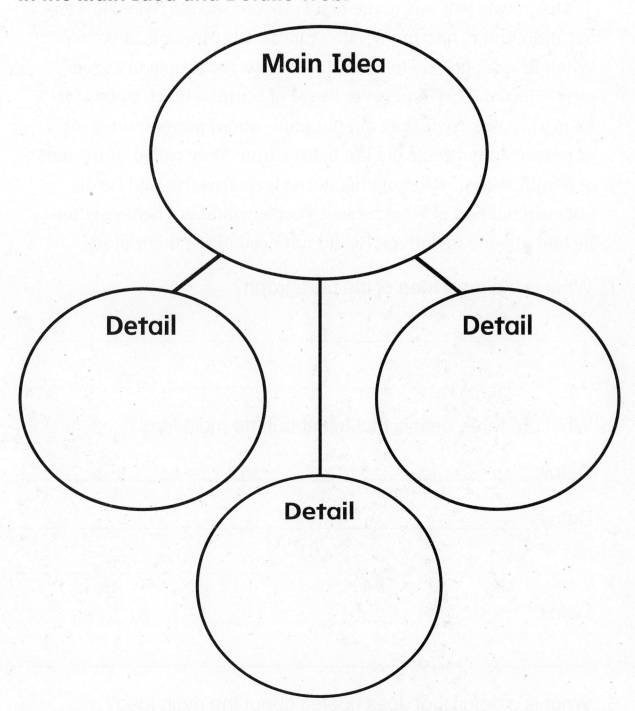

Main Idea

Detail

Detail

Detail

How does the information you wrote in this Main Idea and Details Web help you summarize *Columbus Explores New Lands*?

 At Home: Have your child use the chart to retell the story.

Columbus Explores New Lands
Book 2.2/Unit 5

187

Name _____

Read the paragraph. Then answer the questions.

Marco Polo was one of the first Europeans to see Asia. He went to China, India, and many other places. His trip took 24 years. When he got back, he told remarkable stories. People in Europe were amazed. They had never heard of burning black stones for heat. That was coal! They did not know about paper money, silk, or pasta. Many people did not believe him. They called him "man of a million lies." He swore his stories were true. He said he did not even tell half of what he saw. People would not believe what he had already told them. He did not need to tell them more!

1. What is the main idea of the paragraph?

_____

_____

2. What are three details that tell about the main idea?

Detail: _____

Detail: _____

_____

Detail: _____

_____

3. What is a detail that does not tell about the main idea?

Detail: _____

© Macmillan/McGraw-Hill

At Home: Work with your child to read a short article and find the main idea and several supporting details.

Read the paragraph. Then answer each question.

If you were a sea explorer, you would spend plenty of time on a ship. You could stand on the <u>bow</u> and look ahead to search for land. You could walk back to the <u>stern</u> and watch if a whale swam by. A sailor on the <u>starboard</u> side of the ship might see some pirates coming from the right. If so, you better run over to the <u>port</u> side to see if they are on the left side! You might even climb the <u>mast</u> to get a better look from above. Every night you climb down the <u>hatch</u> and sleep below.

1. What are a bow and a stern?

_____

2. What are starboard and port?

_____

3. What do all the underlined words have in common?

_____

4. What clues helped you to know what the underlined words mean?

_____

_____

At Home: Have your child draw a picture of a ship and label the parts with each of the underlined words in the paragraph.

Name _____

A. Answer each question.

1. How would you find information on the Internet about explorers in the South Pole?

_____

_____

_____

2. What would you like to learn about explorers? How would you find information on the Internet to answer your question?

_____

_____

_____

B. Explain what each term is below.

3. search engine _____

_____

4. key words and phrases _____

_____

_____

5. URL _____

6. home page _____

At Home: Ask your child what he or she would type into a search engine to learn about America before Columbus came.

Name _____

As I read, I will pay attention to the pronunciation of the vocabulary words.

	Around 3,000 years ago, Greece and the city of Troy were
10	at war. Legends say that 10,000 Greek ships made a sea
20	**voyage** to attack the city at the edge of Turkey.
30	The war between Greece and Troy lasted 10 years. It ended
40	when some Greek soldiers hid in a huge wooden horse. They
51	tricked the people of Troy into pulling the horse inside the city
63	walls. Then the Greek soldiers attacked the city.
71	Years later, many people who heard the story thought
80	that Troy was not a real place. German archaeologist Heinrich
90	Schliemann (SHLEE-man) changed their minds. In 1871, he
97	began digging at a small hill on the coast of Turkey. He found
110	the remains of nine ancient cities buried inside the hill. One
121	city had large stone walls. The **vast** city looked the same way
133	Troy was described in legends.
138	Schliemann found treasure hidden inside a copper jug. 146

Comprehension Check

1. How did the war between Troy and Greece end? **Main Idea and Details**

2. Did it take long to find the remains of nine cities? **Make Inferences**

	Words Read	–	Number of Errors	=	Words Correct Score
First Read		–		=	
Second Read		–		=	

At Home: Help your child read the passage, paying attention to the goal at the top of the page.

Columbus Explores New Lands
Book 2.2/Unit 5

Name _____

**A. Write a short paragraph about exploring new lands.
Use at least five words from the box.**

away	Asia	along	America	ahead
afloat	across	afraid	ago	around

_____

_____

_____

_____

**The Latin root word *ped* means "foot." Use the root word
and its meaning to write meanings for the words below.**

pedestrian: _____

_____

pedal: _____

_____

At Home: Have your child check the definitions for the
words above by looking them up in a dictionary.

Figure out the missing word in each sentence. Each missing word has a silent *k, g, w,* or *b*. Write the word on the line. Then circle the silent letter in each word you write.

1. A car should stop at a stop _____.

2. A _____ is a very small buzzing insect.

3. A _____ is a cutting tool.

4. What is not correct is _____.

5. A _____ is a finger.

6. To print your name is a way to _____ your name.

7. Your _____ is part of your leg.

8. If you _____ the right answer, you are correct.

9. Clothes that need to be ironed are _____.

10. To go up a mountain, you must _____.

At Home: Help your child look for words with silent letters in books, newspapers, or magazines.

The Ugly Vegetable
Book 2.2/Unit 5
193

Name _____

Find and circle the six vocabulary words. Then match each word you find to a clue below. Write the word on the line.

```
B   L   Q   T   T   J   C   P
M   L   T   R   A   D   E   R
U   E   O   N   I   O   N   I
S   A   R   O   M   A   W   C
C   O   R   N   M   R   N   K
L   X   T   R   R   I   V   L
E   T   S   O   N   I   N   Y
S   C   E   N   T   B   N   G
```

I. This is a smell. _____

2. This is a pleasant smell. _____

3. These are the parts of our bodies that move our bones.

_____

4. This describes something that is flowering and growing.

_____

5. This describes something that has small, sharp thorns or points.

_____

6. This is the exchange of one thing for another. _____

At Home: Have your child write the words not circled. They are: *corn* and *onion*.

Name _____

As you read *The Ugly Vegetables*, fill in the Sequence Chart.

First

↓

Next

↓

Last

How does the information you wrote in this Sequence Chart help you summarize *The Ugly Vegetables*?

At Home: Have your child use the chart to retell the story.

Write a sentence that tells what is happening in each
picture. Use the words *first, next,* and *then.* Then write a
sentence that tells what happens last. Draw a picture to
go with your sentence.

1.

_____

_____

2.

_____

_____

3.

_____

_____

4.

_____

_____

At Home: Ask your child to tell about today using the
sequence words: *first, next, then, after that, later, last,* or
finally.

© Macmillan/McGraw-Hill

As I read, I will pay attention to the punctuation in each sentence.

	Many scientists believe the first corn was grown in Mexico
10	more than 6,000 years ago. Corn helped change how people
19	lived.
20	Before corn, people found food by hunting animals and
29	gathering wild plants. People would move when there was no
39	more food left in a place. And they moved often. But then
51	people learned they could grow corn by dropping seed into
61	the ground. They became farmers and moved less often.
70	Some Native American groups grew corn. They knew they
79	had to settle in **areas** where corn grew well. So they picked
91	places that had rich soil, water, and sunshine. Growing corn
101	was hard work. People gained **muscles** as they planted and
111	cared for the corn. The **aroma** of cooked corn filled their villages.
123	These Native Americans planted their corn in the spring.
132	Then they picked, or harvested it, in summer. They learned
142	many different uses for corn. 147

Comprehension Check

1. Before corn, what did people do when there was no more food left in a place? **Problem and Solution**
2. Describe areas where corn can grow well. **Description**

	Words Read	–	Number of Errors	=	Words Correct Score
First Read		–		=	
Second Read		–		=	

At Home: Help your child read the passage, paying attention to the goal at the top of the page.

**Write a pair of homophones from the box to complete
each sentence.**

horse	knew	right	deer	weight
write	hoarse	dear	wait	new

1. Dad _____ Laura would be thrilled with a

   _____ guitar for her birthday.

2. They must _____ on line to enter the "Guess the

   Elephant's _____ Contest."

3. Whitney couldn't ride her _____ because she

   was still _____ from her cold.

4. I sent _____ Auntie Lee a letter telling her about

   the _____ I saw in the backyard.

5. He can't _____ with his _____
   hand.

At Home: Help your child make up sentences for favorite
homophones.

© Macmillan/McGraw-Hill

Name _____

A. Cross out the silent letter in each word.

gnu	thumb	design	wren
wrote	knife	gnome	knead
wrong	gnash	knot	wrestle
write	know	wring	knowledge
doubt	knight	climb	gnarled
gnat	knob	wrinkle	knapsack
gnaw	crumbs	knee	sign
assign	comb		

B. Use at least five of the words above to write a short story about something that happens in a garden.

_____

_____

_____

_____

_____

_____

At Home: Challenge your child to name other words that include silent letters.

A. Check each thing on the list you know how to do.

___ Make a sandwich   ___ Fix a snack

___ Take care of plants   ___ Make leaf or potato prints

___ Play a game   ___ Sprout beans

B. Pick one thing you checked. Write directions for it. Be sure your directions are in order.

Follow These Steps to _____

Step 1: _____

_____

Step 2: _____

_____

Step 3: _____

_____

Step 4: _____

_____

Step 5: _____

_____

 At Home: Have your child draw a picture to illustrate each step in the directions he or she wrote.

Name _____

Follow the directions below.

1. Write at least five words that have the **hard *c*** sound.

_____

_____

2. Write at least five words that have the **soft *c*** sound.

_____

_____

3. Write at least five words that have the **hard *g*** sound.

_____

_____

4. Write at least five words that have the **soft *g*** sound.

_____

_____

At Home: Encourage your child to write a short story using
any of the *soft* or *hard c* or *g* words.

Name _____

A. Write the meaning of each vocabulary word.

1. spacecraft _____

2. footprint _____

3. surface _____

4. discovered _____

5. visible _____

6. lunar _____

B. Write a story about the moon using all the vocabulary words from above.

_____

_____

_____

_____

_____

As you read *The Moon*, fill in the Classify and Categorize Chart.

Observing	Visiting

How does the information you wrote in this Classify and Categorize Chart help you summarize *The Moon*?

© Macmillan/McGraw-Hill

At Home: Have your child use the chart to retell the story.

The Moon • **Book 2.2/Unit 5** 203

Follow the directions below.

1. Write your two favorite pastimes? They could be sports, hobbies, or any other thing you enjoy doing.

_____

2. Pick one of the pastimes you wrote above. List some of the things you know about this pastime.

_____

_____

_____

3. Reread your list above. Circle each thing that tells something about how to do the pastime.

4. Use the items you listed to write a paragraph about how to do this pastime. Add more information if you need to.

_____

_____

_____

5. Now reread your paragraph. Cross out any sentence that does not tell how to do your pastime.

At Home: Play a game with your child in which you get points for every one of a certain type of thing you see.

As I read, I will pay attention to tempo and the pronunciation of the vocabulary words and proper nouns.

	On July 20, 1969, astronauts Neil Armstrong and Edwin
7	"Buzz" Aldrin landed on the moon. Their boots made
16	**footprints** on the **lunar surface**.
21	There is no weather or water on the moon. So rain will not
34	wash the footprints away. And air or wind will not blow them
46	away. The footprints may be **visible** for millions of years.
56	The moon is close to earth. You can see the moon easily
68	with just your eyes. But there is much more to see in the night
82	sky. You just need the right tools.
89	A telescope helps people see things that are very far away.
100	You may use a telescope to see all of the bumps and craters
113	on the moon. You might also see some planets. Planets are
124	large bodies that move in a circle around the sun.
134	The night sky is also full of stars. A star is a ball of
148	burning gas. 150

Comprehension Check

1. What is one way to classify the planets in our solar system?
   Classify and Categorize

2. How do you know this piece is not fiction? **Author's Purpose**

	Words Read	–	Number of Errors	=	Words Correct Score
First Read		–		=	
Second Read		–		=	

At Home: Help your child read the passage, paying attention to the goal at the top of the page.

In some **compound words** the smaller words often give clues to the word's meaning. Other compound words mean something slightly different.

A. Think about the meaning of each compound word in the box and the meanings of the two small words that make it up. Write the compound word below the heading that best describes it.

upset	bedroom	birthday	daylight
online	haircut	headset	outfit

1. Meaning comes from the two smaller words

_____

_____

_____

2. Meaning does not come clearly from the smaller words

_____

_____

_____

B. Use at least two of the words above in two sentences. Write them on the lines below.

3. _____

4. _____

At Home: Have your child look through magazines or books to find compound words and write two of them in a sentence.

Find and circle each word in the box in the puzzle below.
If they have the soft *c* sound, shade the words blue.
Shade the words yellow if they have the soft *g* sound.

across	again	carry	cycle
energy	face	frog	game
gem	gentle	good	wagon

```
w   c   y   c   l   e   n   g   g   e   j   a
g   p   p   n   m   o   h   e   s   l   f   c
e   m   g   o   g   a   m   m   c   t   s   r
n   e   v   a   h   b   g   l   e   n   t   o
t   m   w   c   a   r   r   y   t   e   a   s
l   h   a   n   g   e   a   f   r   o   g   s
e   i   n   k   s   y   g   c   w   z   x   t
l   a   y   d   g   q   a   f   r   a   h   p
c   a   r   r   f   b   i   f   g   o   o   d
y   y   e   h   a   q   n   k   t   o   s   b
c   n   x   d   c   x   n   i   g   a   m   e
e   n   o   z   e   x   h   r   e   m   h   b
```

© Macmillan/McGraw-Hill

At Home: Have your child write a story using *hard* or *soft c*
or *g* words on this page.

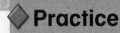
Name _____

Write a story about the nighttime, a storm, or a topic that
you find exciting. Use personification and imagery in
your writing. Then draw a picture that shows some of the
imagery and personification you used in your story.

_____

_____

_____

_____

_____

_____

_____

_____

© Macmillan/McGraw-Hill

 At Home: Read poetry that uses personification or imagery
with your child.

A. Imagine that you are an astronaut. Write a diary entry about your life. Use the words in the box.

distant	vast	planet	voyage	spacecraft	lunar

_____

_____

_____

_____

_____

B. Use two words from the box to complete each sentence.

blooming	ranger's	warning	aroma

1. The _____ of _____ flowers made me smile.

2. We shared the _____ _____ about the approaching storm with other hikers.

Name _____

Use the words in the box to complete the crossword puzzle.

surface	agreed	gathered	noise	signal
knit	trade	afraid	giant	round

Across

3. use yarn and two needles
   to do this

4. an exchange

5. collected

8. an unpleasant sound

10. said yes to something

Down

1. scared

2. extremely large

6. the shape of a circle

7. the top layer

9. a sign, action, or gesture used
   to communicate

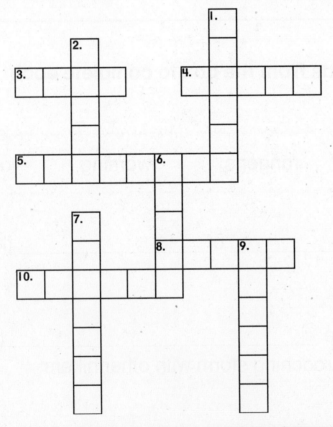

Name _____

Search the puzzle for the words in the box. Circle each word as you find it. Then write it under the correct column below.

badge	hinge	large	fudge	merge
urge	judge	edge	orange	cartridge

```
h  a  m  e  r  g  e  o  j
h  i  n  g  e  c  x  r  u
m  u  l  d  k  s  f  a  d
n  b  a  d  g  e  u  n  g
c  a  r  t  r  i  d  g  e
p  t  g  d  u  r  g  e  m
a  s  e  d  g  e  e  n  g
```

Words ending with *dge*

_____

_____

_____

_____

Words ending with *nge*

_____

_____

_____

Words ending with *rge*

_____

_____

_____

At Home: Have your child write sentences using five of the words in the box.

Name _____

A. Complete each sentence with a word from the box.

> forgetting   simmered   assembled   devoured   menu   fetch

1. The stew _____ on the stove for two hours.

2. My dog can _____ the newspaper.

3. Ken _____ the food before anyone else could eat.

4. The waitress gave us a _____ to look at.

5. Billy kept _____ his jacket at school.

6. Shin _____ the chairs in three rows.

B. Use the words from the box to make up sentences like the ones above.

1. _____

2. _____

3. _____

4. _____

5. _____

6. _____

Name _____

As you read *Mice and Beans,* fill in the
Reality and Fantasy Chart.

REALITY	FANTASY
What Could Happen?	**What Could Not Happen?**

How does the information you wrote in this Reality and Fantasy
Chart help you to better understand *Mice and Beans*?

At Home: Have your child use the chart to retell the story.

© Macmillan/McGraw-Hill

Read the book titles and look at the illustrations. Write
fantasy **or** *reality* **to tell what kind of book it is. Then**
write a sentence that explains how you know.

1. _____
_____
_____

2. _____
_____

3. _____
_____

4. _____
_____

At Home: Invite your child to draw a book cover for a reality
story and one for a fantasy story.

© Macmillan/McGraw-Hill

As I read, I will pay attention to the pronunciation of foreign words.

	"Can you bring me the ang pow packets, Ling?" her mom asked.
12	Ling picked them up. She loved getting her ang pow on New
24	Year's Day. The packets bulged with a gift of money in them.
36	Ling looked at her bright red piggy bank. She dusted it off,
48	and thought about the money she would be adding to it. The
60	pig smiled. He enjoyed this time of year, too!
69	Her aunt and uncle arrived with her two cousins, Betty
79	and Bobby. Everyone was dressed in his or her best clothes.
90	The children were given their ang pow packets. Then they
100	snacked from the Tray of Togetherness.
106	"Ling did all this while I was getting ready," said her mom,
118	giving her a hug.
122	"Lucky for us, Ling has been a big help," said Ling's dad.
134	Everyone was happy to go to the New Year's Day parade. 145

Comprehension Check

1. Where are Ling and her family about to go? **Character and Setting**

2. How do you know that Ling will get money this New Year? **Make and Confirm Predictions**

	Words Read	–	Number of Errors	=	Words Correct Score
First Read		–		=	
Second Read		–		=	

 At Home: Help your child read the passage, paying attention to the goal at the top of the page.

Name _____

Write the definition for each verb. Then add the word ending *-ed*, *-ing*, or *-s* to each verb and use it in a sentence. Write the sentence on the lines.

I. gather _____

gather + s _____

_____

2. invent: _____

invent + ed _____

_____

3. combine _____

combine + ing _____

_____

4. imagine _____

imagine + s _____

_____

© Macmillan/McGraw-Hill

At Home: Have your child look through books
and find words ending with *-ed* or *-ing*.

Name _____

A. Think of at least one word that has the same ending as each word below. Write the word on the line.

1. large _____

2. range _____

3. judge _____

4. cage _____

5. indulge _____

B. Write a silly poem using at least four words from above.

_____

_____

_____

_____

_____

At Home: Ask your child the definition of each word.

Name _____

A. Think about something simple that you know how to do. Write directions to tell how to do it. Be sure to give your directions a heading.

You can write directions for:

• solving a math problem.

• something else you like to do.

_____

_____

_____

_____

_____

_____

_____

_____

B. Have a classmate read your directions and try to complete the steps. Change your directions if you have to.

At Home: Have your child write directions that tell how to clean his or her room.

Name _____

◆ **Practice**

r-Controlled Vowels:
ar, are, air

A. Add a letter or letters at the beginning or the end of the letter groups below to create as many words as you can.

ar

1. _____

_____

air

2. _____

_____

are

3. _____

_____

B. Choose one word that you wrote from each group. Use each word in a sentence. Write the sentences on the lines.

4. _____

5. _____

6. _____

At Home: Have your child use two of the words from the page to write a short paragraph that tells how authors and illustrators probably feel about their work.

Stirring Up Memories
Book 2.2/Unit 6   219

Name _____

Write a paragraph to tell the story shown in the pictures.
Use all the words from the box.

memories	imagination	familiar
glamorous	creating	occasions

_____

_____

_____

_____

As you read *Stirring Up Memories*, fill in the Conclusion Chart.

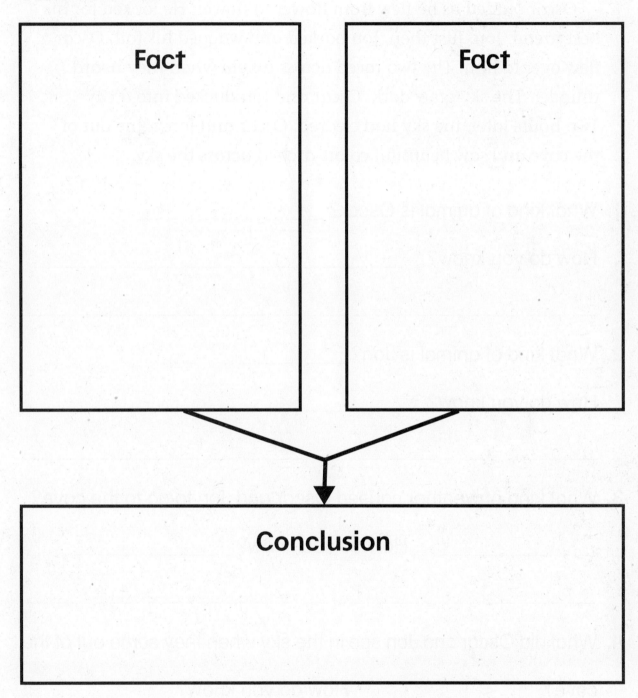

Fact	Fact

Conclusion

How does the information you wrote in the Conclusion Chart help you summarize *Stirring Up Memories*?

 At Home: Help your child use the chart to retell the story.

Read the story. Then answer the questions.

Oscar buzzed as he flew from flower to flower. He looked for his best friend, Jon. Just then, Jon barked and wagged his tail. Oscar flew over to him. The two raced across a field when they heard thunder. The sky grew dark. Oscar and Jon ducked into a cave. Two hours later, the sky had cleared. Oscar and Jon came out of the cave and saw beautiful colors arched across the sky.

1. What kind of animal is Oscar? _____

   How do you know? _____

   _____

2. What kind of animal is Jon? _____

   How do you know? _____

   _____

3. What kind of weather caused Oscar and Jon to go to the cave?

   _____ How do you know? _____

   _____

4. What did Oscar and Jon see in the sky when they came out of the

   cave? _____ How do you know? _____

   _____

At Home: Talk with your child about what conclusion you would draw if he or she saw a person sweating while walking away from a basketball court.

© Macmillan/McGraw-Hill

As I read, I will pay attention and copy tone and expression.

	A shutterbug is someone who takes photographs. Taking a
9	photo is not hard. Usually you just have to point the camera and
22	push a button.
25	Photos keep **memories** alive. They help us remember
33	**occasions**, such as birthdays and weddings. Photos also help tell
43	us about the past. Old photos tell us what people wore, what they
56	did, and how they lived.
61	Some people have jobs as shutterbugs. They take amazing
70	photos with special cameras, and people pay them for their work.
81	Some photographers work for newspapers. Their photos
89	show events that have happened around the world. Other
97	photographers take photos for magazines. Their photos may
105	advertise products or add information to an article.
113	Photographers may work indoors or outdoors. Some even work
122	underwater or in the air. A lot of photographers have their own
134	style of taking photos. These photographers may become famous
143	because their photos show us new things. 150

Comprehension Check

1. What is a "shutterbug"? **Main Idea and Details**

2. Why is it important to take pictures? **Make Inferences**

	Words Read	–	Number of Errors	=	Words Correct Score
First Read		–		=	
Second Read		–		=	

At Home: Help your child read the passage, paying attention to the goal at the top of the page.

Name _____

**Read the root meanings and definitions in the box.
Then answer the questions.**

Root	Definition	Word	Definition
graph	write	**autograph**	sign your name
cycl	circle or ring	**bicycle**	something with two wheels that you ride
act	do	**actor**	someone who is in a play

1. How does the root **act** help you know the meaning of **actor**?

_____

2. How does the root **cycl** help you know the meaning of **bicycle**?

_____

_____

3. How does the root **graph** help you know what **autograph** means?

_____

_____

4. Which word from the box tells something writers do in

bookstores when people buy their books? _____

At Home: Tell your child that *phon* is a root that means *sound*. Ask why it makes sense that *phon* is a root of the words *telephone* and *microphone*.

Name _____

Write a silly sentence that includes all the words in each row.

1. far   jar   star

_____

_____

2. care   share   spare

_____

_____

3. air   pair   stairs

_____

_____

4. card   yard   hard

_____

_____

5. rare   stare   square

_____

_____

6. bark   mark   dark

_____

_____

At Home: Have your child draw three stairs and write an *air* word from the page on each stair.

A. Answer each riddle with a word that has onomatopoeia.

1. Balloons make this sound when they burst. What is it?

_____

2. Lions, bears, and tigers make this sound. What is it?

_____

3. Car horns and geese make this sound. What is it?

_____

4. Snow can make this sound as you walk on it. What is it?

_____

5. Rain makes this sound as it hits the ground. What is it?

_____

**B. Use at least two of the words you wrote to write a
poem. The poem does not have to rhyme.**

_____

_____

_____

© Macmillan/McGraw-Hill

At Home: Ask your child to use the words *zip, buzz,* and
chirp to tell you a short poem. The poem does not have to
rhyme.

Choose the words from the box that belong in each column below. Write the words on the lines.

peer	fern	fear	sincere
term	gear	jeer	steer
clerk	year	clear	where

1. *-ear* as in *near*

_____

_____

_____

_____

2. *-eer* as in *deer*

_____

_____

_____

_____

3. *-er* as in *verb*

_____

_____

_____

_____

4. *-ere* as in *here*

_____

_____

_____

_____

© Macmillan/McGraw-Hill

At Home: Have your child think of words that rhyme with the words in the box.

Name _____

Write a story about art or an artist. Use all the words from the box.

| talent | treasures | impossible | pleasant | watch |

_____

_____

_____

_____

_____

_____

_____

_____

At Home: Challenge your child to tell a story using the words in the box.

© Macmillan/McGraw-Hill

**As you read *Music of the Stone Age,* fill in the
Make Judgments Chart.**

What I Know	What I Read

Judgment

How does the information you wrote in this Make Judgments
Chart help you to better understand *Music of the Stone Age*?

At Home: Have your child use the chart to retell the story.

Music of the Stone Age
Book 2.2/Unit 6

229

© Macmillan/McGraw-Hill

Name _____

Read the story. Then answer the questions.

The class was on a field trip to a big, crowded art museum. Polly and Abe stopped to see some wooden masks from Africa. When they looked up, lots of people were there, but their class was gone. Polly and Abe were lost!

They agreed to stick together. But Abe wanted to go looking all around the museum for their teacher. Polly wanted to talk to a guard and then stay in front of the masks, where they last saw their class. While Abe and Polly were trying to agree on a plan, their teacher appeared. She looked as glad to see them as they were to see her!

1. Could Polly and Abe have done anything to keep from getting lost? If so, what?

   _____

   _____

2. After they got lost, what did Polly and Abe do right? Explain.

   _____

   _____

3. Who came up with a better plan for solving the problem of being lost, Abe or Polly? Explain your answer.

   _____

   _____

   _____

At Home: Reread the story and discuss with your child what he or she would have done if in Abe or Polly's place.

Name _____

**Use a word from the box to complete each sentence.
Use each word twice.**

glasses	check	break	iron	sticks

1. Peanut butter _____ to the roof of David's mouth.

2. Will you _____ to make sure the light is off?

3. This gate is made of _____.

4. I wash the plates and _____ after dinner.

5. If you're tired, you can take a _____.

6. The teacher put a _____ next to George's name.

7. Danya built a little house out of _____.

8. Viv wears _____ when she reads.

9. Dad has to _____ a shirt for work.

10. I will _____ my pretzel in half and share it
with you.

© Macmillan/McGraw-Hill

At Home: Give two meanings for a simple multiple-meaning
word and ask your child to guess the word.

Music of the Stone Age
Book 2.2/Unit 6

231

Read the dictionary entry and the encyclopedia entry.
Then answer the questions.

Dictionary Entry:	Encyclopedia Entry:
klez•mer (klez'-mər) *noun* joyful, fast-paced folk music that started in Eastern Europe. We danced to a klezmer band at Aunt Sarah's wedding.	**Klezmer** is a lively form of Jewish dance music. It comes from Eastern Europe. Most klezmer bands have a singer, violins, flutes, bass, drums, and cymbals. Klezmer means instruments of song in Hebrew.

1. If you read the word *klezmer* in a story and wanted to know what it meant, how could you find the meaning most quickly?

   _____

2. Which source gives more detailed information about klezmer

   music? _____

3. How could you best find out whether the word klezmer is a verb

   or a noun?_____

4. If you didn't know what cymbals were, how would you find out?

   _____

5. How would you find the correct page for the word klezmer in a
   set of encyclopedias?

   _____

   _____

At Home: Work with your child to use a dictionary or the internet to learn what these reference sources are: *thesaurus* and *database*.

© Macmillan/McGraw-Hill

As I read, I will pay attention to the pronunciation of the vocabulary words.

	Puppet shows are a tradition in many parts of the world.
11	Some countries have theaters that perform only puppet shows.
20	Puppet shows can be used to teach history and other
30	lessons. People teach with puppets all over the world.
39	Banraku (BUHN-rah-koo) puppets have been used to tell
47	stories and teach Japanese history for more than 300 years.
56	Three puppeteers are needed to move some Banraku puppets.
65	One controls the head and right arm. Another puppeteer
74	moves the left arm. The third puppeteer moves the feet. Some
85	puppets even have eyes that move. **Watching** Banraku
93	puppets is almost like watching a real person move.
102	Banraku shows first began in Osaka, Japan. The stories
111	performed by the puppets often show everyday life in Japan.
121	The characters may be rich or poor. The settings are villages,
132	cities, or castles. Banraku is as popular now as it was more
144	than 300 years ago. It is one of Japan's greatest **treasures**. 154

Comprehension Check

1. What can puppet shows be used for? **Main Ideas and Details**

2. Where and when did Banraku shows first begin? **Main Ideas and Details**

	Words Read	−	Number of Errors	=	Words Correct Score
First Read		−		=	
Second Read		−		=	

At Home: Help your child read the passage, paying attention to the goal at the top of the page.

Music of the Stone Age
Book 2.2/Unit 6

233

Write six sentences about the picture. Use at least one word from the box in each sentence.

fears	steers	her	here	there
hearing	ear	serves	cheering	where

1. _____

2. _____

3. _____

4. _____

5. _____

6. _____

 At Home: Have your child say sentences about the picture using the words not used already.

Name _____

A. Circle the words that have the same vowel sound in each row.

1. cord   cone   snore   work

2. our   roar   for   torch

3. frost   sport   boar   coat

4. store   star   core   stare

5. tore   born   roast   fork

6. strong   form   horn   hurt

7. soar   sour   cork   verb

8. wore   score   turn   drop

B. Write four sentences using words that you circled above.

9. _____

10. _____

11. _____

12. _____

At Home: Have your child make up riddles that use words with *or, ore,* and *oar*.

Name _____

**Choose a word from the box to match each clue.
Write the words to complete the puzzle.**

powerful	allowed	products
design	instrument	invented

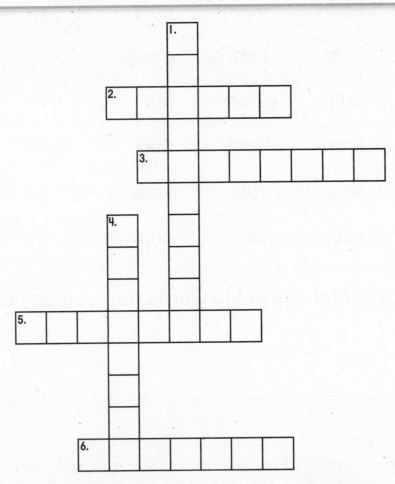

Across

2. a plan for making something

3. things made by people or machines

5. created something new

6. made something able to happen

Down

1. a tool made for a special purpose

4. very strong

© Macmillan/McGraw-Hill

Name _____

As you read *African-American Inventors,* fill in the
Compare and Contrast Chart.

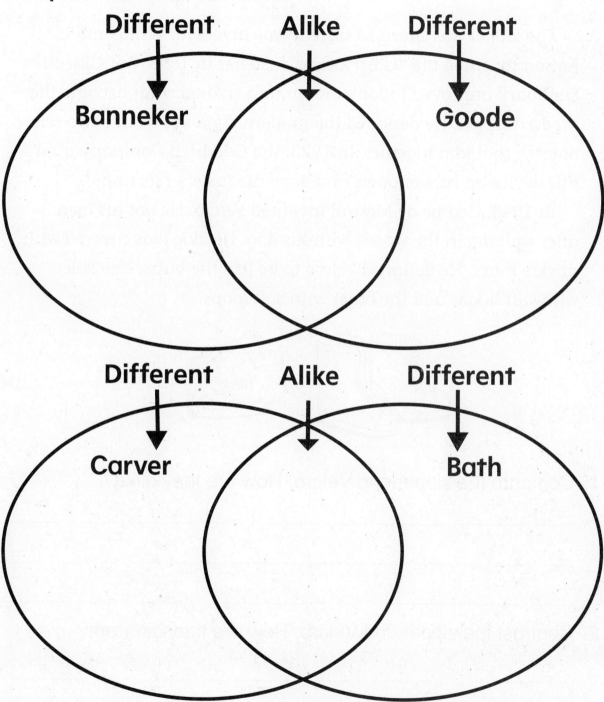

Different   **Alike**   **Different**

Banneker   **Goode**

Different   **Alike**   **Different**

Carver   **Bath**

© Macmillan/McGraw-Hill

How does the information you wrote in this Compare and Contrast
Chart help you to better understand *African-American Inventors*?

🏠 **At Home:** Have your child use the chart to retell the story.

Read the passage. Look at the pictures. Then answer the questions.

The zipper has changed since it was invented. Whitcomb L. Judson invented the "clasp locker" fastener in 1893. But Gideon Sundback improved Judon's design and created what became the modern zipper. He designed the modern zipper to be like two sets of teeth that join together. In 1923, the Goodrich Company used this device on rubber boots and gave the fastener its name.

In 1948, George de Mestral invented Velcro. He got his idea after walking in the woods with his dog. His dog was covered with prickly burrs. He designed Velcro to be like the burrs, one side with stiff hooks and the other with soft loops.

1. Compare the zipper and Velcro. How are they alike?

_____

_____

_____

2. Contrast the zipper and Velcro. How are they different?

_____

_____

_____

© Macmillan/McGraw-Hill

African-American Inventors
Book 2.2/Unit 6

At Home: Ask your child to compare and contrast other everyday things, such as aluminum foil and plastic wrap.

Name _____

As I read, I will pay attention to the pronunciation of the vocabulary words.

9	People have always used tools to make counting numbers easier. Hundreds of years ago, you might have used an abacus
20	in math class. This tool helped people calculate large numbers.
30	Computers began as simple calculating machines. In many
38	ways, a computer is just a faster abacus.
46	The first computer was **invented** in 1623. German
55	scientest Wilhelm Schickard created it. Other people have
63	invented better calculating machines since then. But none of
72	them looked like the computers we know today.
80	The first person to invent an electronic computer was German
90	scientist Konrad Zuse. In 1941, he built the Z3. The Z3 could do
102	calculations much faster than any other **instrument**. It was the
112	first computer that could run a program. A program is a set of
125	instructions that tells a computer what to do.
133	The best-known early computer was ENIAC. It was built in
143	1946. It was a giant machine that calculated quickly. 151

Comprehension Check

1. How was the first computer different from computers today?
Compare and Contrast

2. Were there electronic computers before 1941? **Draw Conclusions**

	Words Read	−	Number of Errors	=	Words Correct Score
First Read		−		=	
Second Read		−		=	

At Home: Help your child read the passage, paying attention to the goal at the top of the page.

African-American Inventors
Book 2.2/Unit 6

Name _____

A. Try to add *-ful* and *-less* to each word to make a new real word. Be careful. Not all words will be real words when you add the suffixes.

1. power

_____

_____

2. thought

_____

_____

3. help

_____

_____

4. wonder

_____

_____

B. Write a paragraph about something you would like to invent. Use at least two words you wrote above or two new words that have the suffix *-ful* or *-less*.

_____

_____

_____

_____

_____

At Home: Help your child use some of the other words they wrote to describe characters from favorite stories.

© Macmillan/McGraw-Hill

Name _____

A. Write related words from the box to complete the story. Then circle the words in the story with *or, oar, ore*.

believe	believable	unbelievable	disbelief
allow	allowed	allowance	allowing

A reporter for the school magazine watched in amazement.

The score was even. The crowd roared in _____

at the ref's last call. The ref was _____ the other

team to take another timeout. "That's _____!"

Nora yelled.

"How many timeouts are _____ in this sport?"

the reporter asked Nora. Nora had to whisper the answer

because she'd screamed herself hoarse.

The reporter left the game. On the way out, he saw kids

spending their whole _____ on tee shirts and

hats. The reporter thought, "I need to learn more about this

game. I wonder who invented it. I'm going to find out."

At Home: Have your child circle and list related words he or she finds on one page of the newspaper. Challenge your child to use the words in sentences.

African-American Inventors
Book 2.2/Unit 6

241

Make a time line of your life. Write your date of birth in the first box. Write this year's date in the last. In between, add the dates of other important events. You might want to add events like these: the birth of a younger brother or sister, moving to a new house, learning to ride a bike, taking your first plane ride, or hitting a home run.

I was born on
_____

I am in the
2nd grade in
_____

 At Home: Have your child talk about the time line. Ask him or her to explain what was special about the events included.

© Macmillan/McGraw-Hill

Name _____

A. Write as many words as you can that have the same vowel sound spelling as each word listed below.

I. *ure* as in *lure*

_____

2. *ire* as in *tire*

_____

3. *ier* as in *direr*

_____

B. Write a rhyming poem using at least four of the words you wrote.

_____

_____

_____

_____

At Home: Together, write a mystery using *-ire* and *-ure* words.

Name _____

Use all the words in the box to write a letter to a friend about going to a soccer game. Use the picture below for ideas.

goalie　figure　vendors　concern　collection　exclaimed

Dear _____,

_____

_____

_____

_____

_____

                              Sincerely,

                              _____

**As you read *Babu's Song*, fill in the Character
and Setting Chart.**

Characters	Setting

How does the information you wrote in this Character and
Setting Chart help you to better understand *Babu's Song*?

At Home: Have your child use the chart to retell the story.

Babu's Song • **Book 2.2/Unit 6** ◆245◆

© Macmillan/McGraw-Hill

Think about a story. Think about who its characters might be, when and where the story would take place, and what might happen. Use these questions to help you to develop your story.

1. What is the name of the main character?

_____

2. What is this character like?

_____

_____

3. What does this character like and dislike?

_____

4. What problems does this character have in the story?

_____

_____

5. Where and when does your story take place? Describe this place.

_____

_____

At Home: Encourage your child to write the story for which he or she has brainstormed a character and a setting.

© Macmillan/McGraw-Hill

Name _____

As I read, I will pay attention to the punctuation in each sentence and to the tempo.

	Emily's newest **concern** was that each student had to join a
11	sports club. She and Kate wanted to join a walking group. Lists
23	were pinned to a board in the hallway at lunchtime.
33	A crowd of students stood in front of the lists. Emily slowly
45	moved closer to the board. She looked up at the collection of
57	lists. The lists were all placed so closely together. The crowd
68	pushed her. Emily scribbled her name and backed away. She
78	was glad that the job was done.
85	Two days later, Emily had an even bigger worry. She learned
96	that in her rush to sign a list, she had put her name on the
111	field hockey list!
114	"But Miss Sims! I don't know anything about field hockey!"
124	Emily **exclaimed** to her gym teacher.
130	"I'm sorry, Emily," Miss Sims said. "The walking group is
140	full anyway. This is a good chance to learn something new!" 151

Comprehension Check

1. What is the setting of this scene? **Character and Setting**

2. Did Emily mean to sign up for field hockey? **Make Judgments**

	Words Read	−	Number of Errors	=	Words Correct Score
First Read		−		=	
Second Read		−		=	

© Macmillan/McGraw-Hill

 At Home: Help your child read the passage, paying attention to the goal at the top of the page.

Name _____

Write a word on each line to complete the story. Choose words that will create a story that starts out sad and ends up happy. Use the position and meaning of the other words to help you figure out words to write.

Once there was a _____. She was very

_____, but she didn't have a

_____. "What should I do?" she wondered. "I

must _____ a _____."

Suddenly she had an idea! She could _____ to

get the money for a _____. In fact, if she did

that, she might even have enough for _____!

She immediately set to _____ to get

the _____.

Success! It wasn't long before she _____ all the

_____ she needed.

At Home: As your child reads aloud to you, help him or her notice the meanings of the text around unfamiliar words. What clues does that text offer the reader?

A. Circle the words from the box in the puzzle below.

| acquire | cure | desire | fire | hire | lure | picture |
| pure | require | sculpture | spire | sure | wire | |

```
r  w  p  x  h  j  s  u  r  e
e  i  i  u  m  a  c  t  s  v
q  r  c  b  r  t  u  m  o  d
u  e  t  u  d  e  l  f  g  e
i  x  u  o  r  k  p  m  r  g
r  q  r  p  v  e  t  i  b  s
e  s  e  e  h  l  u  r  e  p
h  i  r  e  u  q  r  o  j  i
c  i  k  m  c  n  e  p  s  r
f  j  d  a  d  e  s  i  r  e
```

B. Circle the word part that is the same in the set of related words. Then write a sentence that explains how you think the words are related in meaning.

I. dental   dentist   dentures

_____

At Home: Invite your child to use each of the words above orally in a sentence.

Babu's Song • Book 2.2/Unit 6   249

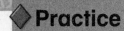
Make a map of your bedroom. First create symbols for each label in the key. Then draw a map of your room to show where each item is located. Create new labels and symbols for items not listed in the key.

Key

bed =

door =

dresser =

closet =

At Home: Look at maps in an atlas with your child. Find the key or legend and read the labels to find out what each symbol means.

Name _____

**A. Write an answer to each question. Use the words in
dark type in your responses.**

1. What are two special **occasions** you enjoy?

_____

_____

2. What musical **instrument** would you like to play?

_____

3. What sport would be **impossible** for you to play?

_____

_____

4. Do you have a **collection**? What do you collect or would like to
collect?

_____

5. What are two favorite family **memories**?

_____

_____

6. What foods do you look for on a restaurant **menu**?

_____

Use all the words in the box to complete the story.

concern	tired	pleasant	fetch	vendors	products
familiar	perfect	devoured	judges	allowed	pair

Our family couldn't wait for the fair on Saturday. At first

we had some _____ about the weather. Luckily,

it turned out to be a _____ spring day.

All the _____ arrived early. Each one

was _____ to set up one table. Some

_____ for sale were _____ .

Others were new and unusual. At one table Dad found a

_____ of _____ lamps for the den.

The fair had a contest to see whose pet could

_____ the most tennis balls. The

_____ laughed the whole time. Dad was

so hungry, he _____ two hot dogs. We went

home _____ , but happy.